P9-DDD-832

PEOPLE ❀ IN PALESTINE

Books by Olivia Coolidge

❁ OLIVIA COOLIDGE

PEOPLE ❁ IN
PALESTINE

1 9 6 5

HOUGHTON MIFFLIN COMPANY BOSTON

The Riverside Press Cambridge

COPYRIGHT © 1965 BY OLIVIA E. COOLIDGE

ALL RIGHTS RESERVED INCLUDING THE RIGHT TO REPRODUCE

THIS BOOK OR PARTS THEREOF IN ANY FORM.

LIBRARY OF CONGRESS CATALOGUE CARD NUMBER 65-19985.

PRINTED IN U.S.A.

CONTENTS

INTRODUCTION

THE WORLD can never repay the Jewish people for its great gift to civilization. We perceive this fact today, but in the time of Jesus, the treasures of Jewish scripture were little understood. The Roman rulers of Palestine were highly conscious of their great debt to the Greeks. For the Jews they felt tolerance or contempt. The great Augustus believed that within the framework of the Empire, each nation should follow its own customs. Accordingly, he granted the Jews a number of privileges which did credit to his good intentions. They were, for instance, exempted from military service, since Sabbath-keeping would have been impossible there. Instead of emperor-worship, a daily sacrifice was offered in the emperor's name at the Jewish Temple. Jewish communities in pagan towns had their special rights, and in some cases self-government. The protection of Roman power was extended to their Law.

For all these concessions, the government felt, Jews ought to be grateful. It angered a succession of emperors to discover that they were not. In 66 A.D., the nation rose against its rulers and had to be put down. It was necessary to raze their Temple to the ground, destroy Jerusalem, and extinguish the Jews as a nation. Yet still they caused trouble.

Looking back over history at the situation, we may easily see that the Jews were not perverse. Their position was in truth intolerable, partly for reasons which the Romans never understood, and partly for ones they could not alter. Thus the age of Jesus is an age of ferment. Growing tension is producing splinter parties inside Judaism. The Voice of John the Baptist is raised, calling for repentance. Other voices demand revolution. Let the people rise, remembering past times when the Lord protected his own. More worldly voices preach compromise;

more gentle ones preach resignation. But universally, all know these are times of oppression. An explosion in which the bitter extremists prevail is the terrible outcome—unwise, unappealing, yet inevitable. There comes a moment when decency and common sense are swept away, when only courage and fanatic devotion count. These, too, are annihilated at last; but the Jewish people picks itself up out of the ruins and goes on, in some respects strengthened.

What were, then, the grievances of the Jews which made their position intolerable? The Jews were, in the first place, a people of single-minded devotion living in an age of compromise and under an Empire which was actively encouraging common culture. The very nature of the land and government made their separate position an almost impossible one. In the first place, they themselves were divided. Judaea had a Roman governor. Galilee and outlying parts were under sons of Herod, half-foreign princes whose Jewish religion was highly compromised by pagan culture. This naturally bred faction, besides introducing Graeco-Roman shows, games, temples, and polyglot people under government patronage. Such admixture was easier because in any case the Jews were not the only inhabitants of the land. Samaria, for instance, contained half-Jews with a rival religion. The Greek Decapolis, a community of ten Greek cities scattered beyond Jordan, was Syrian as much as pure Greek. Thus the tendency of nations to mingle could not be controlled and was officially encouraged. Meanwhile, the Jewish religion, though tolerant toward converts, was adamant in its opposition to gentiles. Their very touch polluted. All that they owned, or sold, or made was simply unclean. Their community baths, their naked athletics, their gladiatorial shows were as offensive as their temples, actually planted in cities half-Jewish, half-Greek and disputed by both parties. We live in another age of mingling and may find this Jewish position unsympathetic. It is unfair to condemn it, however. The Jewish religion was indeed worth preserving. The separatist efforts of this tiny corner of the world had a permanent value which we may comprehend today, though the Romans could not.

A second cause of distress was economic. The Jewish Temple was one of the greatest in the world. The Jewish priesthood for that time has been estimated at twenty-four thousand, not counting the Levites, also unproductive. This vast apparatus of worship was supported out of the taxes enjoined by Mosaic Law, amounting to close to 40 percent for Jewish farmers. Judaea is an unfertile land, yet above these levies came the taxes of the local rulers, be they Philip or Antipas or Pontius Pilate. Small wonder that there was misery among the poor. The marvel is that in spite of this there were rich. The times, however, bred wealth, especially from commerce. Those who trafficked unscrupulously with the heathen, dined with Romans, invested in the great tax-farming concerns grew very rich. A cleavage developed between the Jews themselves no less disastrous than that which separated them from the gentiles.

The traditions of the Jews increased these hatreds. They had always been a warlike people. The glorious history of their rebellion against Alexander's successors was fairly recent. Since this had been born of resisting hellenization, Jews naturally thought it a victory for their God over the kings of the world. All the difficulties of the hellenistic kings with Rome and Egypt which had loosened their grip on the Jews were not considered. Thus the pattern of delirious rebellion was already established. Since nothing was wanting but a leader, it naturally followed that one would arise from time to time, trusting in the Lord and perfectly ready to fall upon lukewarm Jews as well as heathen. Writers whose names have vanished fed such aspirations by "prophetic" visions attributed to Moses, but mirroring their own times. In these, a victory of the forces of right, the coming of a King Messiah, or the end of the world were variously depicted.

Such was the nation the Romans attempted to govern, not always wisely. The special privileges granted by Augustus were vital to the life of the Jewish people, yet they depended on the personal whims of an emperor who might be the mad Caligula or the monster Nero. The Roman governors, whom we hear of mainly through Jews, all have a bad name—some worse than others. Most of them probably did their best, but were facing an impossible task for which their breeding and habits made them unfitted. It is, if anything, a tribute to them that rebellion did not come sooner.

Our period, then, has a beginning with the birth of Jesus and an ending with the great revolt of A.D. 66–70. Most strangely for the background of a messenger of love, it is dominated by hatred. It is also, however, a time of universal longing, a moment when the world is not at rest. The individual finds himself at the mercy of large forces—political, spiritual, economic—which he cannot control. These throw him back on the resources of his own soul, which he had not yet learned to explore. The Jews alone have a clue, but they are confused. They do not know whether their kingdom is of this world or beyond it. Some say one thing, some another. All in their own way are about the Lord's business. They are desperately, tragically, gloriously in earnest. There is no frivolity in them.

In such an age, stories can only pick out details. The confusion in the mind of a poor shoemaker may illustrate that of the times. The dependence of a young man's marriage on the life or death of people in far-off Rome gives an example of the helplessness of ordinary men. The true nobility of the best of the Pharisees is as well worth noting as the weaknesses which Jesus pointed out. Individuals make up this age. Their problems are universal ones which have endured. In them if anywhere lies the explanation of the spread of the Christian religion. Their questions, confused though they might be, demanded an answer.

Prologue

A ❀ ❀ WISE
MAN'S ❀ ❀
QUESTION

About 6 B.C.

THE CARAVAN came into Gerasa by the late afternoon, heralded by a horn blown at the gate of the city. In the fast-growing town of the Gerasenes, any arrival of a caravan was an event, since trade was its business. Gerasa lay in the hills beyond Jordan, looking out onto the Syrian desert which, like a great neutral sea, separated the Empire of Rome from that of the Parthians on the Euphrates. By the wisdom of Augustus there was peace, so that over desert highways traveled uninterrupted caravans, bearing westward ginger and cinnamon from India, lapis lazuli from Persia, silk from China, brought over distant steppes by two-humped camels to the marts of Mesopotamia. Eastward too went the trade, carrying Egyptian linen, Grecian pottery, Syrian brass or copper ware, but principally gold and silver. The wealth of the Roman Empire spiraled dizzily, so that people had a hunger for luxuries and money to buy them. All this traffic ran through Palmyra, neutral city of the desert, whence a part of it turned southward through Gerasa, either traveling to Petra, rose-red city of rocks, on its way to Egypt, or else across Jordan into Palestine. Meanwhile, Arabian traffic came up from Petra, bearing frankincense and myrrh or gold and ivory, African treasures on their way to the ports of Tyre and Sidon.

The town of Gerasa, athwart these routes of trade, received all people. Jews from Babylon came on their way to the Temple, often conveying the tribute from their communities. Greeks, Bedouins, Arabians, Syrians, Roman detachments on holiday from a nearby encampment jostled one other on Gerasa's streets, either spending money or selling every kind of rest and refreshment. Gerasa in fact was all things to all people. It even had three names. The Greeks, whose language it mainly spoke, called it Gerasa. To the Syrians and Arabians, it was Jerash. To the Roman Empire at large, it was known as Antioch-on-the-Golden-Stream, to distinguish it from other Antiochs, of which there were several. In similar fashion, the great temple of the Luck of Gerasa, which was being enlarged in the center of town, belonged to a moon goddess known to the Greeks as Artemis, to the Syrians as Atargatis, Mother of All, to the Arabs as Allat. The sacred precinct at the south gate was dedicated to Olympian Zeus, in other words to the Syrian Baal. Meanwhile, the north gate, through which the caravan was now winding, was named in honor of Arsu and Azizu, the caravan gods, who were the morning and the evening stars, called by the Greeks Castor and Pollux.

Inside the north gate at the head of the great central artery of Gerasa lay the Little Caravanserai, by no means as ambitious as the Great Caravanserai at the other end, but yet a fair open space surrounded by booths, warehouses, and stables. Here donkey drovers were offering to carry wares over Jordan more cheaply than by camel. Food and drink for man or beast were on sale, as were mats for bedding, more comfortable than the bare ground. Touts of every description were proffering lodgings in the town, a show of dancing girls at a tavern, a slapstick comedy performed in the south theater in honor of a local festival. Entertainments of a still more dubious sort were hinted at with a wink and a quick sentence behind the back of a hand, accompanied by a nudge and a knowing grin. Inside the caravanserai itself an Indian sword-swallower, an Egyptian female contortionist, a bellowing strong man, and a pair of jugglers were already at work; while a company of Gerasene beggars and light-fingered thieves circulated busily. Everywhere, wares were being offered for sale: souvenirs of the temple, new shoes, camel harness, inlaid daggers, and trinkets which might tempt a traveler's fancy.

In the midst of this hustle and bustle, the incoming caravan began to sort itself out. Most of it belonged to the companies of great Palmyra merchants, who provided the caravan leader and its camel hands as well as the chief supplies. They also rented out camels to travelers and, for a small fee, allowed others to join the train on their own mounts. Thus, as the caravan wound to a halt, it split quite naturally into its component parts, each differently suited. In a sense all wanted the same things: room to stable the camels, a place to lay merchandise where it would be safe, a chance to wash off dust, to rest, and take refreshment. Those, however, who were the professional travelers had their arrangements, which included their own storehouses and guards. They had also their connections in the town and soon departed, eager to pay their respects to the Luck of Gerasa and to sample the enjoyments which the city offered. The smaller groups among the travelers remained guarding their own wares, as did the camel hands or servants. Most of the latter gravitated toward the entertainers, who presently put up a ring of torches and increased their numbers by a pair of very low comedians, as well as musicians and dancers.

From all of this the individual travelers drew apart, chiefly grouping themselves in a half-finished portico at the upper end which had been intended for the reception of those who kept their gear beside them. As the sun went down and the stars came out in the sky, the booths around the caravanserai shut up. What remained of buying and selling was concentrated around the ring of entertainers in the low-lying part. These being too noisy to allow sleep, the group in the portico was sitting rather than lying, conversing in the manner of half-strangers who quite idly exchange remarks on what may come into their heads.

"You meet all sorts on the trail," said a Syrian merchant, setting his back against a pillar and drawing up his knees. "Where do you come from?"

"Rome," said an Arab unexpectedly. "That is, by way of Antioch-on-the-Orontes. My master, whose

freed slave I am, is in his turn the freed slave of a
Roman financier and has charge of his interests in the
eastern trade. I was sent out by them to find a trust-
worthy agent in Palmyra, since our old one grew rich
at our expense and served us little."

"All Palmyrenes are thieves," said a Greek sourly.
Judging by this man's worn robe and sandals and by his
belligerent air, one might imagine that he had failed in
life and was resentful of his fortune. At all events, nobody had the hardihood to inquire what he was doing
coming down the eastern trail. A silence fell.

"Gerasa is a fair city," remarked a Babylonian in long
robes, brightly embroidered, yet rubbed and soiled with
travel. "Or so the captain of the caravan was telling
me. They are paving the central part of their great
street with marble, and colonnades are springing up
along it. In our country we build in a different fashion."

"Gerasa is all talk," remarked a Jew, who was also
from Babylon, going to the Temple. He had drawn
himself to one side to eat his provisions, wash his hands,
and say his prayer. But either in Babylon Jews did not
hold so strictly apart, or perhaps his own nature was
gregarious. At all events, he had hitched himself a
little closer and broke into the conversation. "Everything in Gerasa is either half-finished or scarce begun,
so that imagination will serve you better than your
eyes to look around."

"That will not always be so," the Syrian argued.
"In any case, the Golden Stream is very pretty, since

it runs right through the town and does not dry in summer. At this season, moreover, it really does run gold with the sand washed through the valley when there has been heavy rain."

"The Golden Stream is hardly even a river," pointed out the Jew disdainfully. "As for the buildings, even were they finished, they are not to my taste. They are of course in the heathen style."

As everybody present was, in the sense in which he used the term, a heathen, the conversation dropped again. Nobody, at the end of a long day, desired to quarrel.

"What are *they* doing?" asked an Egyptian suddenly. He had proved himself an exceptionally close-mouthed man hitherto, giving no explanation of his presence. Secretly he was an agent of King Herod of Judaea, who had extensive trading interests which he did not boast about, since they were more profitable than kingly. On this occasion, surprise that the Egyptian had spoken directed attention to the spot he indicated. Two more Babylonians had edged themselves outside the portico and were sitting in the open, saying nothing and apparently staring at vacancy, save that occasionally one would turn to the other and murmur solemnly in his ear, whereupon the second would bend forward slowly to scratch something on the ground with a pointed stick.

Everyone looked at the Babylonians. They were impressive figures with long beards, nicely oiled and set in curls. Upright in carriage, they were nevertheless surprisingly old for the fatigues of a desert journey. The beard of one of them, in fact, was snowy white; while that of the other, though dyed a jet blue-black, was so much at variance with the lines on his wrinkled face that he seemed even older.

"My teachers?" asked the first Babylonian. "They count the stars."

One of the camel hands, an ignorant Bedouin who had no business to speak in such a company, or even to listen, exploded in a loud, sudden guffaw. For the thing was ridiculous. It was one of those clear nights when there is no moon and the stars jostle one another for space in the sky, each pinpoint revealing a host of smaller ones behind, receding into infinite distance until the brain reels. It becomes a question as to whether the blackness of night is not an illusion, so completely is it dusted within and without by the brilliance of stars.

"All knowledge," the Babylonian added unperturbed, "is written in the stars, and these men read it."

"You do not yourself do so, I perceive," said the Arab-Roman smiling.

"Alas, my skill is less; and perhaps my interest in the people whom I meet is also more. Yet I, too, can cast a horoscope which will tell me all manner of things unknown to me before."

"Tell me my fortune!" With sudden eagerness the Greek bent forward. "My birth date . . ."

The Babylonian shook his head. "Those calculations take much time."

"I might have known you would find an excuse,"

cried the Greek bitterly, "considering that it is plain I can offer no money."

The Babylonian made no answer to this insult, save to look silently away from the group toward his two compatriots, as though withdrawing himself into their company.

"You may tell me something instead," said the Arab-Roman, who had learned through being a slave how to make himself pleasant. "My horoscope may not need so much work, for it is famous. In the day and the hour of the birth of great Augustus, I was born."

"Why, then, you are a wise and prudent man whom your employers do well to trust with their negotiations. You love justice, are righteous in anger, but do not hold a grudge. One blow fortune has dealt you, for you do not beget sons."

"Now that is a remarkable piece of fortune-telling!" exclaimed the Greek dryly. "For the character of Augustus is common knowledge, while no one would refuse to admit such a complimentary likeness. As for his daughters, our friend was loudly lamenting them upon the journey."

"I see you have probed me to the depths," said the Babylonian laughing. "The truth is I am no charlatan with clever tricks, but a serious student of the destiny of man and the plans of God. I cannot impress you by any skilled performance, but I will if you care to listen tell you a story from which you may glean truth. Besides, in its fashion the tale has relevance to our present journey."

The offer met general approval. The Syrian stretched out his legs as though to get comfortable, the Egyptian nodded. Even the Jew hitched closer, while the Greek said grudgingly, "I confess I am curious to hear your wisdom."

"Very well," agreed the Babylonian. "My tale is about King Darius, the Great King, he whose dominions stretched from the Hellespont to the end of the world."

"I never heard of him," the Egyptian said.

"And yet he ruled Egypt. Why, the Great King's dominions extended so far that it was a three-months' journey from the outer edges of them to his capital city. And Darius himself was a mighty man befitting his kingdom. Sparks crackled in his beard. When he stamped his foot in anger, it sunk right up to the knee. Two servants were needed to carry his bow and quiver of arrows. None but he could bend that bow, and his shot was unerring as far as eye could see, clear to the horizon. Nor was he less mighty in peace than in war, for he loved justice more than ease. Instead of sitting in pomp in his capital city with wives about him making merry with music or wine, he was always traveling through the length and breadth of his kingdom by horse or by camel, by donkey or by oxcart, sometimes even on foot and in a simple disguise, that he might learn of his subjects and do justice.

"In this way it happened that as he was walking through his kingdom, he came one evening to a cave. And in the mouth of it, fixing his eye on the evening star which had just arisen, sat the prophet Zarathustra."

This time the Babylonian's audience stirred, and the Greek inquired hesitatingly, his tongue stumbling over the foreign word, "You mean Zoroaster?"

The Babylonian nodded. "Even he. This was the great Zarathustra who knew the one God by His holy name, or at least by one of His names. For he called Him Ormazd, and He is also Bel . . ."

"And Baal," the Syrian agreed.

"And Dushara," the Arab said.

"And Zeus, the Olympian . . ."

The Greek made a contemptuous sound at that. "Not He! He is the World Soul, as say our philosophers."

"He is none of these things," pronounced the Jew, who was still sitting outside the circle of the rest. "He is the Holy One of Israel, blessed be He. All others are false idols. Only through Israel can the one true God be approached."

"That is as it may be," said the Babylonian, pacifically. "At all events, Zarathustra knew what we all inwardly confess, that God is one. What is more, he knew the ministers of God, who are the angels, the stars, the lesser gods — Azizu, Arsu, Atargatis, Luck of Gerasa, and all the others. If not by their names, by their functions he knew them. Furthermore, he knew the great archfiend and all the host of demons . . ."

"Pass over that," said the Egyptian, hastily making a sign to avert the evil eye. "This Zarathustra, then, was

sitting in a cave mouth when King Darius came striding by."

"Even so," the Babylonian agreed again. "And
Zarathustra called out, 'Good evening, King Darius,
second greatest of all the kings that are, what are you
doing?'

" 'Walking through my kingdom,' said Darius
shortly, not too pleased at being discovered beneath his
disguise of a poor man.

"The prophet nodded. 'And doing what is written
in the stars,' said he.

" 'And doing justice,' King Darius argued.

" 'I wonder,' the prophet said. 'For what is justice?
Tell me, therefore, what you did.'

" 'I came to a poor cottage,' the king said, 'and begged
for bread; but the peasant cursed me and bade me go
away.'

" 'For his son lay dead within of a fever,' the prophet
said.

" 'I spoke to him again,' the king went on, 'in the
name of God; but he cursed God. Yet I asked him a
third time in the king's name. When he cursed the king,
I hit him with my fist in anger. This was treason,
and he deserved no less.'

" 'This man's son went into the city,' said the
prophet, 'to present a petition at your court, King.
He gained his request, but there he caught a fever and
reached home only to die. Therefore the father in
frantic grief railed on both God and the king.'

" 'I did not know that,' admitted the king. 'I repent my anger, more especially because I am a mighty man, and my fist dashed his brains out.'

" 'You did what was written in the stars,' the prophet said.

" 'I came to another cottage, where sat a man at work on a bow. When I asked him for bread and water, he rose up and brought me goat cheese and olives as well, even pressing on me a draught of sour vinegar-wine from his small store.'

" 'What did you do then?'

" 'I gave him a gold coin which I had about me. It was riches such as he had never expected to see in his whole life.'

" 'You killed one man for treason,' said the prophet. 'Yet you rewarded this man, who was actually at work on the bow which will take your life.'

" 'Now I did not know that either,' said the king.

" 'It was written in the stars. What else did you do?'

"The king thought over his day for a brief moment, and a gleam came into his eye. 'I passed a young man beating an old man. The old man cried to me to rescue him from his impious son, who was beating him half to death.'

" 'And what did you do then?'

" 'Why, I passed by and left them to it.'

"Zarathustra raised his eyebrows in what looked like surprise. 'Did you not consider the crime of a son against a father worth punishing?'

"The king smiled broadly in triumph. 'No, for the young man told me he was not the other's son and had been robbed by him into the bargain.'

" 'And you believed the young man rather than the old one?'

" 'Indeed I did so,' said the king, grinning openly. 'For I knew him. He was in fact my own son, though I never acknowledged him because his mother was of insufficient rank for my harem.'

" 'He was not your son,' said the sage, folding his hands. 'His mother deceived you, hoping to establish a claim on you. And the young man knew this.'

" 'Now this is all very well,' protested the king, with difficulty holding onto his temper. He could see by now how the conversation was going, and he was not used to being bested, even in argument with a prophet. 'I will admit you know more facts than I do. Yet within the limits of those I comprehend, I strive to do justice. On this striving are all my actions based, not on the stars.'

"Zarathustra smiled. 'Shall I give you this day over, King Darius, second greatest of all the kings that are? Since you repent of what you have done, now go and amend it.'

" 'That I will gladly undertake to do,' agreed the king.

"Then Zarathustra stayed the sun in his course and turned him about to reel eastward over the heaven. The stars and the moon likewise retraced their steps in a single flaming instant. Men blinked, astonished, while between the closing and the opening of their eyes, rivers ran backward, rain regathered itself from the earth, and all things disposed themselves as before. As pale dawn glowed in the east, Zarathustra said, 'Here is the day, O King Darius. Awake!' With that, Darius woke up where he had done so on the previous morning; and he started out on his travels again across his kingdom. By the time the evening star appeared, he came to the cavern where Zarathustra sat, just as before.

" 'Now tell me what you did,' said Zarathustra, 'to the man who cursed both God and the king and refused you dinner.'

" 'I told him,' said the king, 'that I was heartily sorry that his son had died as a result of visiting my court in search of justice. In return, I promised him whatever he wanted in compensation, if it were in my power to give.'

" 'What did he ask?'

" 'He prayed me to take his life so that he need not face a lonely old age. Therefore I smote him with my fist, since there was no weapon handy, and dashed his brains out.'

"Zarathustra smiled into his beard, but he made no comment, merely asking, "What did you do to the man who was making a bow?'

" 'I asked him for whom he made the weapon; and he answered that he made it for sale, as he made many others, without knowing into whose hands it might come. Therefore I rewarded him as I had done before. He deserved no less.'

" 'And you did not even destroy the bow?'

" 'Am I a child,' asked Darius haughtily, 'that I should care about the weapon? It is the arm that draws the bow that matters.'

"Zarathustra nodded. The king, whose embarrassment was mounting, did not stay for further questions, but hurried on: 'I may as well declare that when I came to the quarreling pair, I again did as before. I told the young man that he was no son of mine, and he answered that he was not even the son of that woman. Her child had died in infancy, whereat she and her husband had adopted a neighbor's son in its place, hoping to foist him on me as my own and make a profit from him. When I did not acknowledge the child, they revenged themselves on him by many a beating, for which he hates them.'

" 'You did what was written in the stars,' said Zarathustra.

" 'I must admit that may be so,' agreed the king. 'Yet I could have changed my actions; and I confess that I was sorely tempted to do so, merely to get the better of you in argument, O prophet. I thought, however, that it was beneath me to do anything but justice. Tell me, therefore, how can it be that what I do is written for me, while yet I choose it myself?'

"Zarathustra shook his head. 'This, O king, I cannot tell you. For it is the great mystery of religion that things are all fated, and yet all in our own hands. None can comprehend it, not even I, Zarathustra, nor the angels and ministers of God, but only the Highest of All.'"

"That is a good saying," the Greek said softly. No one seeing him now with his keen face alight, would have thought him the same person as the shabby, embittered adventurer on his travels none knew precisely whence or whither. "I have debated that very question in our philosophic schools, but found no answer."

"Our rabbis know the answer," said the Jew positively. "All knowledge is contained in the books God gave to Moses, provided always that they are studied aright."

"Now whether your rabbis indeed know everything," said the Babylonian, "I doubt, since they themselves confess they do not. Yet there are none from whom I have learned more, save only my teachers."

"B-but then," cried the Jew, actually stammering in his eagerness at finding someone in an unfriendly world who understood him, "you must be a hearer of the Word." Unconsciously he moved a little further into the circle. "You attend our synagogues."

The Babylonian nodded. "I also dispute with your wise ones, yet they have never told me how fate and free will can be reconciled."

"These problems are too lofty for me," remarked the Syrian frankly. "Indeed, I must confess the All-High God is too. For practical purposes, I worship the divinities around us."

"And so do I," agreed the Arab-Roman. "It answers better. What has the All-Highest to say to a freed slave? Now Arsu and Azizu have their function. When one is in a caravan, they take an interest."

"That is so," agreed the camel hand hoarsely, muttering his thoughts aloud to himself. "Arsu and Azizu are mighty stars, yet not too proud to shine for the poor."

"Now that indeed is well said," replied the Babylonian, turning to him. "It is true that these stars give direction in the desert to all who need their aid. It is natural, moreover, for the humble to worship a godhead which stoops to meet their need. What is the majesty of the awesome God of Gods to them? They cannot conceive it. Is that not so?"

His tone was kindly, but the camel hand, as much embarrassed by praise as he would have been by blame, had turned over on the ground and buried his head in his cloak. A pause ensued.

"I, too, am a practical man," said the Egyptian at last. "Like everyone else, I try to get ahead. For that reason, if I had been King Darius, I should never have engaged in argument with the sage. I should rather have asked him at once why it was that he called me 'second greatest of all the kings that are.' For if another king arose who was greater, he would very soon make an end of King Darius."

The Babylonian laughed. "I see you understand kings! King Darius by no means neglected to take up that point with Zarasthustra before he went on his way. But Zarathustra assured him that the star of the greatest king had not risen yet.

" 'That is good news as far as it goes,' King Darius persisted, 'but I had intended to leave my kingdom to my son — and he to his son. It is small consolation that I may live out my own reign if my successors are to be swallowed up in the maw of a greater king yet.'

" 'What would you do, then,' Zarathustra inquired, 'if I were to tell you that at such an hour and spot this king was to be born?'

" 'I should send and kill him,' King Darius answered, 'even if it meant putting every child of the right age in that place to the sword. You need not shake your head at that and reproach me with injustice. Kings have their own law.' "

The Babylonian's audience had stirred, clearly shocked. The Egyptian, however, who was a secret agent of King Herod, nodded. "That indeed is a true saying and worth many mysteries to my mind. 'Kings have their own law.' "

"But who was this greatest king after all?" wondered the Arab-Roman. "Augustus? We longed for peace and order, which he gave us."

"Alexander, perhaps," the Syrian suggested. "He who united West and East."

"You are all wrong," said the Jew contemptuously. "It is none other than the King Messiah, who shall establish the rule of the Chosen of God. For to this end God has revealed himself to Israel. Under our King

Messiah, righteousness shall flourish, all evil shall be overthrown, and the worshippers of idols shall drown in their own blood."

Since it was plain this pleasing picture offered little future to his present company, the Jew's pronouncement found small favor. The Babylonian, however, smiled at him, saying, "I perceive, my friend, that you are of the old school. Yet Hillel, that gentle rabbi, came from Babylon; and today his disciples there do not speak of blood. I have heard Rabbi Nathan talk poetically of the day of the Messiah when the rosebush shall bloom without thorns and the lioness suckle the kid. Of blood and destruction, however, he said nothing."

"I speak as my fathers taught me," said the Jew, defending himself. "Yet Rabbi Nathan is a great name in Israel . . . a great name." He shook his head soberly, seeming to ponder his rash threats. "There are many thoughts on these things," he conceded. Clearly it embarrassed him to retract his words, yet he was making an honest effort to speak truth which had for the first time won him respect from the rest. "Is there not evil in the world?" He appealed to the Babylonian. "And must not the King Messiah trample it down?"

"Now you say well," the Babylonian answered. "It is indeed true that under this greatest king light shall conquer darkness, good overcome evil, and the All-Highest vanquish the Arch-Fiend. More I cannot tell you, save that the time is very near. For look, the star of the King has risen in the west!"

He pointed, and all heads turned in the same direction, half expecting to see one spot swept clear of dazzling pinpoints so that a single star might shine in the blackness. But the myriads of tiny lights mocked their vision.

"It is a small star as yet," said the Babylonian apologetically. "I cannot see it myself, save when my teachers point it out. They, however, have measured the heavens and can tell me that this is indeed a new star which, contrary to nature, rose in the west. It does not, moreover, move with the other stars, but stays steady, hovering over the western horizon. We travel to see what spot it marks and to worship that king."

"Now what surprises me," said the Greek softly, "is that with such a moment at hand when the mystery of the ages is almost within your grasp, you do not even join your teachers in study. Instead, you sit and tell stories to us. Why?"

"You are a man of great perception," replied the Babylonian, gazing at him, "though you prefer to deny your own nature. I did have a reason for lingering to talk instead of searching for what is fixed by fate in the stars above us. I wondered why it was that the king came in our time. Was the world more ready than it had been in the days of King Darius? So I drew out your beliefs and hopes, supposing that I might get an answer to this question."

The Greek laughed, a bitter sound. "An answer from *us?*"

"Even so," said the wise man gently. "An answer

from all of you, not even excepting him . . ." he nodded at the camel hand, who, tired of following things far above his head, had gone to sleep. "Each of you told me something. Perhaps also I shall question others whom I may meet on my journey. For this mystery is not written in the stars after all, but in the hearts of men."

SECTION I
A.D. 1 – A.D. 30

THE ✽
OTHER
SIDE ✽

PHINEAS, the son of Onias the priest, blinked at the
darkness while he tried to remember where he was.
He could hear a voice grumbling in a dull monotone on
the flat roof next door. The hooves of a donkey went
trotting down the street. A scavenging dog snarled
savagely. A man whistled. In the distance, a dull,
clanging sound was going on, like metal struck on metal.
Phineas sat up with a jerk, the pieces of his puzzle falling into place. He was in Jerusalem at the house of his
cousin Simeon, and in the summer bedroom which
Simeon had on his roof. There was nothing different
in this from other years, nothing new in Simeon, in
his house, in those early noises of the city that never
slept. It was only he, Phineas the priest, who had
changed.

He put up his hand, which he could just see against
the grayness outlined in the low oblong of the doorway.
Staring at it, he sleepily wondered at his own body for
still being his. He turned his hand about and spread out
his fingers, feeling the life in them. They neither
quivered nor tingled, were grown no greater, and shone
with no strange light. To tell the truth, nothing

would have startled Phineas more than such a peculiar
miracle; yet in his bemused state the absence of one
was almost disappointing. When a man has fulfilled the
purpose for which he was born, how can he simply get
out of his bed, go down, and greet his cousin, "Peace
be with you."?

He could never remember a time when he had not
felt set apart from his fellows by being born to the
priesthood. His father Onias was noble and nobly
allied, while the choice of the Lord had fallen on him
early. Wealth and office had flowed quite naturally
into his hands. Onias had never needed, like many
lesser priests, to engage in trade. As representative of
the High Priest himself in his district, Onias actually
did draw his income from the people's contributions.
He had never resorted to expedients forbidden by the
Law and only justified by the disappearance of ten of
the original tribes of Israel supporting the priesthood.
Much business came through Onias's hands, but all of
it was concerned with the collection of the first fruits,
the best of the harvest, the tenth of the tithe reserved
for priests, the price of the firstborn, the Temple tax,
and various other levies which paid for the worship of
the Holy One, blessed be He, through His priesthood.
This worship, in fact, was the justification for the
whole of Onias's life, for his riches, his business, his
honor. If he lived like a prince, was he not one of the
elect? And had not the Lord, blessed be He, chosen
him early?

This recognition by God had not increased the im-

portance of Onias in priestly affairs, but it had set upon
it the seal of God's approval. At the daily sacrifice in
the Court of the Priests, when the blood of the lamb
had been poured on the High Altar, the presiding
priest went into the Holy Place through the great
gates fifty feet high and plated with gold, behind the
tapestry woven by Jewish virgins in the four sacred
colors, under the golden vine of Israel, its leaves and
clusters tall as a man. Here in the gloom, lighted by
the gleam of the seven-branched candle on lofty
golden walls, the priest offered incense. Only a tapestry divided his human presence from the Holy of Holies, where in empty darkness brooded the Godhead of
Him Whose Name it was forbidden to utter, blessed
be He. Thence returning through the Veil and the
Golden Gates, while the Temple musicians completed
the psalms for the day, the chosen priest blessed the
people, who prostrated themselves as though to the
majesty of God.

This awesome ceremony came but once in his lifetime to a priest, so great were the numbers of the
priesthood in Israel. To some the lot fell in middle
age, to some in old age. To a few, like Onias, it fell in
early youth. But whether it was given early or late, it
set apart the chosen from the great mass of the priests
in the Temple worship.

To Phineas the Lord had been less gracious than to
his father. For thirty years the two had traveled together to Jerusalem for the weeks of their temple service. For thirty years they had made themselves pure

for the Lord, not merely by ritual baths and washing of hands, but by the sacrifices prescribed at the Temple. Unclean before the Lord of sheer necessity was every man who did not live in the city of God. Defilement, like infection, passed from one to another by touch or contact with any unclean thing. Like dirt, uncleanliness lurked everywhere; but being invisible, it was less easily avoided. Only at the Temple could the worst pollutions be purified. To Phineas, when he put on the white linen garments which were always new for every priest, it seemed as though he also was new, washed, reborn, ready for the call to approach the Lord which never came.

"It will come this year, I believe," Onias always said. He was too gentle and loving a man to reproach his son because the Lord was not with him.

In thirty years, Phineas had learned every detail of the Temple service. He had laid out the garments for the priests, cleansed the sacred vessels, stood on guard by the sanctuary or by the open-mouthed urns where the people cast their voluntary donations. He had filled the lamps with holy oil, laid on the mighty altar the scented logs which kept it always burning. He knew the slaughterer's part of his trade, how to hold a struggling beast, pour blood on the altar, flay and disjoint a carcass, separate from it the perquisites of the priests. He knew by heart every gesture and every stately word of the priestly rituals. He could even remember the psalms of the Temple musicians, in which he took no part.

"The Lord of the World must choose His time. Blessed be His Name," Onias would conclude with a sigh when the first three stars after sunset marked the end of their last day of Temple service.

They used to put on the clean clothes they had brought with them and walk away from the Temple, keeping gingerly to the center of the street, lest a casual contact sully the invisible whiteness of their purity before God. Their cousin Simeon, who was himself a priest, though of a different group for Temple service, would receive them in his little upper room where everything — as far as that could be — was ritually clean. Very early the next morning, father and son woke together in the place where Phineas now sat, called at last, but alone.

"Bring back your purity," Onias had bidden his son when a fracture of Onias's hip had made the journey impossible for him. He had not added, "Your call will come this year," merely because he hoped it would not. Yet this year was the one the Lord had chosen Phineas, when his father lay sick and his own son was not grown. Nobody of his kin had seen his act, as he himself had not seen his father's. "Bring back your purity," the old man had said. That at least Phineas could gladden him with.

They had always come home ritually clean. On one occasion, Simeon's mother had died on the night they spent in his house. It had been necessary for them to return to the Temple and purge away the pollution of her corpse. That year the feast that Onias made on his

return had been greater than ever, as though his sanc-
tity, that precious thing, had been rescued from danger.
All his household vessels had been sterilized for his use
and the very knives reground. But no man could purify
the guests, save by simple handwashing. Onias's purity
had worn off little by little, though the memory of it
sustained him in his high place until the next time of his
service. This year he would have to depend on his
son's. Old, weak, and in pain, he craved reassurance.

Phineas arose and washed himself. He was taking
his leave of his cousin when the watcher on the Temple
top cried, "It is day on Hebron," setting the silver trumpets to wake the echoes. Unhurriedly Phineas and
Simeon began to say the "Hear, O Israel."

It was the duty of the keepers of the Jerusalem
gates to fling them wide at dawn. Since, however,
exact timing meant very little, they usually waited until
the crowd of those going out of the city was large and
noisy enough to command their attention. Phineas,
whose object was to avoid being jostled in the dusk
before the gate by unbelievers or countrymen ignorant
of God's Law, bridled his donkey with care, stowing in
his saddlebags the food his cousin had brought him for
his journey.

He was still too early at the gate. The necessity of
making a good start before the heat had been urgent
with him; while the gatekeeper, it appeared, had over-
slept. He was rattling at the bolts now while a rough-
looking citizen with tangled hair and beard swore vio-

lently at him, though in terms which were permitted by pious extremists.

"One man makes the noise," said a voice in Phineas's ear, "and those other two lurk in the shadows. Can you imagine why they are in such desperate haste to get out of the city?"

Phineas, who had been occupied in setting his donkey between himself and the crowd, started violently in dismay. The man behind him smiled apologetically. "I am of the singers of the Lord, and my name is Jairi. I chanted the psalms at your sacrifice yesterday, son of Onias."

"Peace be with you." Phineas nodded, reassured. He remembered this round little fellow and was conscious that they must have traveled the same road for years, though it had been beneath the dignity of a priest to recognize a Temple servant. At least, however, the man must be ritually clean.

"There they go!" Jairi nodded his head at the crowd pushing out of the gateway. "Why must they be first out? They all wear daggers."

"I wear a knife myself," Phineas shrugged.

"I, too." Jairi opened his cloak to show the weapon stuck clumsily into the sash round his fat little middle. "But it is for show. I am not a dagger man."

It was Phineas's turn to look disturbed. Those zealots who acknowledged no king on earth save the Lord were a dangerous group. Their dagger men notoriously hated the rulers of the Jews as much as the Romans.

He himself was hardly a worthwhile target for these assassins. Old Onias, who might have been, was safe at home. All the same it was strange that such men should be in a hurry. Did they plot something or had they committed a crime in Jerusalem which day might discover?

"What have the dagger men to do with you or me?" he asked defensively.

"Why, nothing." But Jairi tugged uneasily at his beard, which was anointed with a scented oil as though he had feasted yesterday evening. "My cloak," he said apologetically. "It is a good one and only a half year worn. Who knows what such men want? I do not carry much wealth, but there are a few presents . . ." He drooped one eye and stared at Phineas blandly. Temple servants had various ways of making money according to their degree. Phineas himself was above such petty profits and would not have come to Jerusalem without an escort, had he expected to carry home anything of value. All the same, his own cloak was a new one; and his saddlebag was bulging with good clothes he had discarded.

He shook his head incredulously. They were talking, after all, of the Jerusalem road. In thirty years of unadventurous travel he had occasionally heard tales of robberies which turned out to be mere drunken quarrels or acts of private revenge. Times were getting worse. The land was filling with strange fanatics preying on Jew and Gentile alike, but surely only in districts remote from Roman control. The very existence of the Jerusalem cohort should guarantee the safety of the road. Yet there were dagger men in Jerusalem itself without a doubt.

Phineas did not know what to think. He was not personally alarmed, but he did not relish a scuffle against men with unwashed hands and filthy bodies, defiled by eating food which had never paid tithe.

"Two are safer than one," Jairi pointed out. "Robbers fear a noisy struggle and shouts for help. We servants of the Temple may travel together."

He meant that he, too, perferred to keep himself clean. Most of the crowd by the gate had been local people going out to work in the olive groves, to gather fuel, or to pasture goats on the drying grass by the side of the road. The few real travelers were probably not even Jews, since they lacked ritual fringes at the corners of their garments. Not to save his life would Phineas have accepted the company of such men. His heart warmed slightly to Jairi, singer of the Lord. "Come, then," he said. Climbing on his ass, he wrenched its head towards the gateway. Jairi followed.

It was full day when they passed Bethany and began to descend the rocky road which ran winding down the sides of ravines, up over rough saddles, then down again, skirting the base of ancient landslides. Already the olive groves were giving place to scrub, among which an occasional herdsman whistled to his flock of small brown goats. The sun had sucked up patches of mist and was soon blazing on a waste of tangled rocks, protected only by occasional wisps of grass like sparse, dead hair. Far off on the western coast, the hot air rising would be setting up a landward breeze. Here inland, the air only trembled with the liquid shimmer of heat.

It had grown too hot to talk. Each drew his head covering low down across his forehead and rode with eyes half-closed. There was nothing to look at. Even the vultures knew this land was empty of life and left it alone. Incoming strangers would not be met with on the road for hours. Very occasionally when a deeper cleft than usual afforded a vista, one traveler could be seen ahead, plodding slowly at something like their own snail's pace, just keeping his distance.

There should have been nothing in that dead land; but there were flies, buzzing about their lowered heads, crawling over their tight-closed lips and into their eyes. Stolidly, Phineas led on. He knew this wilderness of stone through which the road ran down to Jordan. It would grow hotter yet as baking rocks gave back the glare. Presently no traveler would move. Each must find shelter for himself and for his ass until the sea breeze, which reached Jerusalem by noon, should stir the air. Nothing but night and respite from the sun would cool that wilderness of stone, but a man could rouse himself to struggle through it with the help of the wind.

Already Jairi was groaning to himself when they came to the overhang of a rock which had scooped out a patch of shadow on the ground. "Rest here," he mumbled between closed lips.

Phineas shook his head and pointed. It was no time for long explanations. "Yonder!"

Jairi merely slumped off his ass into the shade of the rock. It barely sufficed him and would not cover two. No doubt his fancied alarms had been sucked out of him like morning mist by the heat. Was it conceivable that the hardiest of dagger men would loiter among these boiling rocks? Phineas left him and toiled a painful half mile on his road.

The effort was great, but the prize was worth it. Not for nothing had Phineas traveled this way for thirty years. He knew a cave, semi-dark and almost cool which, not being visible from the road itself, had remained his personal secret. On the whole he was happy not to reveal it to Jairi, lest on future occasions Onias himself be obliged to share his rest with a Temple servant. Not that Onias would have cared. He could afford to be humble. It was Phineas who was obliged to be defensive of his father.

He stumbled off his ass to pick his way carefully round the base of the conical rock which concealed his cave. Even through his sandals, which were new, he could feel the heat of the stones. Ahead of him lay the welcome darkness. From within it, shatteringly magnified as though by a great trumpet, came a donkey's bray.

Phineas dropped the bridle of his own beast and teetered uncertainly, thrown off balance as though by a physical shock. It had never occurred to him that a fellow traveler might find his private refuge. His imagination immediately peopled the cave with the dagger men or brigands about whom Jairi had shown alarm. That they should conjure a donkey out of this barren wilderness or should lie in wait in his own particular refuge seemed almost credible. Such people were servants of the devil.

"Come in, come in out of the sun," urged a kindly voice from the cavern. "I was expecting you. As I broke my bread this morning, I found a raisin — would you believe it? — a raisin, whole and sweet. What could this betoken but a stranger and a friend? Come in, friend."

"I am a Hebrew," answered Phineas stiffly, taking one slow, hesitating step toward the welcome shadow. The voice spoke Aramaic, but the accent was not the harsh Galilee brogue or the quick, clipped speech of the Judaean highlands. There were people worse than outright Gentiles, bastard peoples who perverted the worship of the Most High God and insulted His priesthood by false priests of their own. The moment of silence which followed his remark confirmed the suspicion.

"I have never had a Jewish friend," said the voice with a faint note of doubt. "Of the Pharisees?"

"Of the priests." Phineas's tone was dry. "Going home after service at the Temple."

"A Sadducee! Hm!" The news was as unwelcome as Phineas had known it would be. "A queer raisin for Theophilos of Sebaste to find in his bread! Come in, priest of the Temple. There is room for both of us with space between. I know your ways."

Reluctantly, Phineas decided he must enter. Greek and Roman Gentiles he knew well. Much in their culture was not precisely forbidden by Mosaic Law, which had known nothing of them. Save at the periods of his ritual purity, Phineas would have been willing to chat in a friendly way with any Gentile, though he would not have shared his unhallowed food or drunk from a wineskin made out of an animal offered to an idol. With these bastard Hebrews from Sebaste and their rival claims on God, he had no traffic. Only his compelling need to get out of the sun forced him to acknowledge that the infidel dog was right. It would not pollute him to sit in the cave for a while, provided the other would leave him alone.

He moved into the shadow and made a business of tethering his ass, taking off him his modest provisions and a skin of water whose stale flavor had been partly disguised by a measure of Simeon's wine. Presently, when his eyes were adjusted to the light, he glanced around and saw with a stab of anger that the other was reclining at his ease against a slab of cool stone which he had imagined would support his own aching back. Theophilos of Sebaste was a man approaching middle age, his thick beard slightly streaked with gray. What could be seen of his face was dark in color, as were his sinewy hands and sandaled feet. He was munching contentedly on a dried fig, pausing to lick his fingers clean of the sticky juice. Beside him lay his waterskin, half concealing a very businesslike short sword of the Roman pattern.

He nodded, following Phineas's glance. "Yes, I got it from the Jerusalem cohort in trade. I follow the army. Soldiers from Sebaste always have a coin or two for a lucky pebble or a charm against the evil eye." He winked unashamedly. "Pick up cheap and sell dear, eh, friend? Trade's trade."

"*I* found no raisin in my bread," remarked Phineas, seating himself on a rock as near the doorway and as far from Theophilos as he could manage. Infidels from Sebaste made up large portions of the Roman forces, for which reason their relations with the Jews were especially bad. Their superstitions of every sort were notorious, as were their traders, collecting all manner of oddities to pander to them.

"Did I tell you so to get money out of you? No, friend, I do not deceive you. There lay my stranger, as warm and sweet as if he had been in the sun. Besides, to tell you the truth, I think we have need of each other. I did not like the look of those who traveled ahead. I am handy with my sword, as a trader needs to be, but I have no fancy for fighting three to one."

Phineas looked him over. His cloak, worn and greasy, his gown, patched on one side and ragged on the other, would be part of a pretence that he was not worth robbing. Some of these glib pedlars were very rich. In any case, he would carry little on his person, relying on bankers' drafts wherever he went. But unlike Jairi, he did not seem a timorous man.

Theophilos broke off another fig from the dried cake beside him. He popped it into his mouth and licked his fingers as before. "I grant what you are thinking," he said, chewing steadily. "No one who intended to rob a fellow traveler would put it off till now. The road has long been desolate enough. But imagine that brigands went to meet somebody coming up to Jerusalem, not going down. If a stranger followed too hard on their heels, what would they do then?"

"Hide in the rocks and let him go past them while they waited for their victim to come up."

"Let him go ahead and describe to the first comer what sort of men he had seen on the road? No, no, my friend . . . What did the little fat man confide to you by the Jerusalem gate?"

Phineas started. Had the fellow got eyes all round his head? These traders were sharp. "He said they looked like brigands or zealot assassins." He found he had been drawn by unwilling inches into a conversation, and he tried to cut it off. "Foolish fantasies! Little men are always cowards!"

"This little man had some reason," Theophilos insisted. "He recognized them."

Blinking silently, Phineas looked at him, incredulous yet impressed.

"He turned quite green. Even in the half-light one could perceive he felt a shock. But he backed away out of sight as if he were hoping his distress would go unobserved."

Phineas remembered how Jairi had appeared behind

him from nowhere when he had thought himself alone.
Jairi had been urgent that they should ride together,
although later he had sat down to rest while Phineas
went on. Perhaps the uneventfulness of the journey
had now convinced him that he had not been noticed.
Phineas cursed himself for becoming involved on this
day of days with infidels, ruffians, and menial servants
of the Temple. "The man has a memory for faces," he
conceded. "He recognized me also."

"Just so."

Theophilos appeared to have finished what he had
to say. He turned his fig cake over, looking for a juicy
morsel. He extracted one, humming a tune. Phineas
turned his back on him, washed his hands, said his
prayer, and set out beside him his own bread and cheese
and figs, the latter fresh ones, firstlings of the market
and very expensive. He started to eat.

He had wanted silence, and yet he found it awkward.
Nothing had been settled. Theophilos, it seemed, intended to travel with him. For his own part, he was
determined to go on alone. It was true that mere travel
together would not pollute him, any more than sharing
a cave or fragments of talk. But he, the son of Onias
the priest, could not without scandal ride home in company with such a man, most especially on the very day
after he had served the Lord.

He tried to fix his mind again on that service and re-
capture the wondering awe with which he had awakened. He had looked forward to this journey as a
lonely one of meditation, preceding the triumph of his

return home. Now, however, his peace of mind was completely eroded. Anxieties which had been no concern of his had been forced upon him.

A notion struck him. "If indeed these men await a traveler," he said with his back still turned, "they must meet him near here on the road when the wind rises. For he will not travel in the heat, nor can they."

Theophilos stopped humming, but said nothing. Clearly he listened.

"Then if we rest for an hour longer than usual we may go our ways in peace. None will molest us."

"And a man may be robbed or murdered while we sit idly here." Theophilos cleared his throat ostentatiously and spat. "You . . . Sadducee!"

He used the honorable name with such a wealth of contempt that Phineas started to his feet in quivering anger. "Infidel dog!" He put his hand to the knife in his girdle, but Theophilos merely raised his eyebrows at the gesture. Clearly he knew the priest would not touch him.

"I would have imagined," Phineas was beside himself with passion, "that filthy heathen swine would speak with more prudence inside the borders of Israel. Men have been lynched for less."

Theophilos sat up with a jerk. "You threaten? Let me warn you that I, too, have my connections. Valerius Albinus, who commands the Jerusalem cohort, is in my debt."

It might be true. The two men glared at each other, but it was Phineas who turned away. The fact was, he felt ashamed of the suggestion that they should do nothing. He had only made it because he had not thought the matter through. How could he give his mind to other men's affairs when he was preoccupied by his own service to God? He knew it was useless to explain this to Theophilos, yet he felt the need of justifying himself.

"You misunderstood me," he said with such haughtiness as he could muster. "There can be no question of our waiting here together. When the wind rises, I shall ride on alone. These men did not see me at the Jerusalem gate. Not knowing me, they will suppose I do not know them. They will lie in their ambush and let me pass unmolested. Why should they not? Meanwhile, you may easily rest two extra hours, or even three. If by that time their victim has not passed, he is not going to Jerusalem today. Their trap will not have sprung. Why should they care if you go down the road?"

"The raisin was a fair omen, priest," Theophilos retorted, "but it was not meant for you. I do not like you. I have no fancy for travel in your company. Suppose, however, these assassins did mark you at the gate. You will be in danger."

"There is a chance." Phineas shrugged with real indifference. "I think they were in too much of a hurry. Nor would I, whatever they threaten, accept your protection."

Theophilos leaned back against the stone and settled himself with a fold of his cloak beneath his head.

"There is a slight risk in the plan, but it has the advantage that we may part company. You may go ahead and deliver your warning while I wait. Meanwhile, since conversation is offensive to us both, I'll go to sleep."

He suited the action to the word. Phineas settled himself near the mouth of the cave to wait for the wind.

He saddled his ass and made off somewhat later, leaving Theophilos snoring. The sun was behind him now, and the cooling wind blew strongly. Refreshed by a short doze and with half his journey over, Phineas sought to regain his exalted mood. He brushed aside the cobwebs of suspicion — thin guesswork, founded on nothing but the fears of Jairi and the conspicuous hurry of three wild strangers at the gate. He might in a joking way deliver a warning to travelers coming up, and yet he hardly knew how to do so lightly. He did not wish to suggest his own imagination had constructed such a lurid tale. He certainly could not admit to having learned it from a man of Sebaste.

On the whole, Phineas thought it wise to decide what to do when he saw what travelers he met with. This left him free to dwell on his homecoming, a chosen priest at last. Onias had never reproached him, never suggested a justification for the mysterious delay of the Holy One, blessed be He. He could not, however, conceal his lifelong disappointment. All his years Phineas had kept the Covenant of Israel, not refining upon it with the new interpretations beloved of the

Pharisees, and yet not questioning its smallest incon-
venience. Faithfully he had kept holy the Sabbath,
performed the rituals, eaten the food God required.
Now at last his reward was here. He would take in
his own strong hands those wasted claws of his father
and would say to him, "I bring the blessing of the Holy
One." He, Phineas, who had never in all the years of
his manhood been head of a household, would sustain
the beloved old man with his strength. The eminence
he had always desired and despaired of would be his.
He saw himself becoming what Onias had been, a ruler
of the people, lifted high by his own worthiness and
God's approval. It almost occurred to him, though he
put the thought away, that he might prove himself
greater than Onias. His was a stronger because a
harsher nature.

So mused Phineas the priest, riding down from high
Jerusalem through the wilderness of stone. Ahead of
him the wind, spilling over the ridge of Judaea, ran
down into the deep hollow where Jordan filled the Sea
of Salt. It rustled through the irrigated gardens of
Jericho and passed over the sickbed of Onias, murmuring in his ear that his son was on the road.

Even as the wind breathed on his father, Phineas
came into view of a short stretch of road where a traveler had discarded a ragged bundle. He felt surprise.
Even rags had a value, and no one poor enough to carry
them at all would leave them behind him. So far had
Phineas's suspicions been lulled by his own train of
thought that even when the bundle stirred, he believed

it a trick of the light. Not for two or three more paces did his eyes disentangle from the disheveled heap the shape of a man.

With a sudden shock Phineas jerked at his donkey, which halted while his appalled gaze took in the bloodstains which he had supposed part of a shadow. That siesta, that involuntary brief doze into which he had fallen in the cave! Had it lasted longer than he had supposed? For the deed was done. The victim lay huddled, knees tucked up, head out of sight between his shoulders, one arm flung wide, the other twisted beneath him. Phineas had thought he moved, but was not sure. He might be dead.

The priest clenched his hands, those pure, clean hands with which he was going down to bless his father. Could he pollute them by examining a corpse? It would be madness and ingratitude to the Lord . . . if the man were dead.

The outflung arm moved, groping. The shoulders heaved and then were still again. Not dead, then. Not absolutely dead. Merely going to die. Had not the Holy One, Blessed be He, sanctified His servant before the nation of Israel? Dare Phineas succour the man, and be left with a corpse on his hands? He thought of Onias and knew he could not take the risk.

Phineas passed by on the other side of the road, very carefully keeping his distance. The way was narrow, and a stumble or a movement might pollute him. There were tears in his eyes as he did so, and he turned his head away. It was not in his nature to be cruel, yet the duty for which he had been born weighed heavily on him.

His action need not make so very much difference. Not far behind Phineas on the road must be the Temple singer. "What matters the purity of a Levite compared to mine?" he muttered aloud. Even as he said this, he knew that Jairi would be afraid. The road was lonely, and who could tell where the assailants lurked? Most certainly Jairi would not dare to render aid. The Samaritan would.

The conviction brought a flood of relief. Why, the very task was a fit one for an infidel dog whose hands had never been clean. What had he to lose? Surely the Lord of the Worlds had chosen Theophilos to spare His priest.

This was a comforting idea, yet Phineas's spirits were not much raised thereby. He would have preferred, he told himself, to act the Samaritan's part. Indeed, he was surprised to feel so deeply his inability to be of use. Such sensations were surely to his credit, yet they brought no peace of mind. He sighed, soberly conscious that he was not as other men were and could not allow himself the luxury of doing as he wanted.

Phineas rode home to his father's house as the sun was dropping behind the Judaean hills. He came quietly, without the parade of welcome he had expected. None of his people were on the lookout, so that he must even tether his own ass in the court before striding in, burdened with the tidings which no one seemed to want.

His steward met him in the entrance. "My Lord, your father . . ."

The servant's face was white, and his voice stumbled. Phineas felt a quick stab at the heart, a mortal blow. He found himself looking down on the hands which he had kept pure for his father by forsaking a man in his need. "When did Onias die?" he demanded slowly.

"It was this afternoon, my lord, when the wind blew. He died at the first breath."

Phineas ought to have torn his garment, but he made no move. He said to nobody and apparently apropos of nothing, "So Onias was dead, then, all that time. One corpse pollutes a man as well as another. I might have stayed."

"My lord," cried the steward, alarmed at his manner, "your father lies dead."

Phineas was still looking at his fingers. He opened them and turned them around as he had done in the darkness of his cousin Simeon's room. With a rather similar sense of slow surprise, he found them the same.

"My lord . . ."

"Take me to my father," Phineas said. "It cannot now matter if I go to him as I am — with blood on my hands."

THE ✸ SHORT STRAW

RABBI JONATHAN consorted with the angels. There was no doubt about it. Even his brother Jakim agreed, although Jakim was burdened with the sole support of their mother from the proceeds of his terraced hillside farm, where ten-foot pockets of earth required retaining walls almost as high. Rabbi Jonathan, as was well known, worked daily for subsistence at the shop of a shoemaker in Jerusalem, devoting five hours of his time to this drudgery because he would take no money for teaching God's Law. Even Miriam, his sister, had no reproach for Rabbi Jonathan, though Miriam was so shrewish that her first two husbands had renounced the burdensome honor of being brother-in-law to a famous rabbi. The presence in the village of two such ordinary brethren as Miriam and Jakim, not to mention half a dozen friends of the rabbi's obscure boyhood, made no difference to the awe and veneration he commanded.

If Rabbi Jonathan had never returned to the village, its admiration for him would have been simple. A dusty little hamlet of the Judaean uplands, never visited save by the gatherers of tax or tithe, it took pride in boasting in the nearest market town of its famous son. And when at the season of the Passover the village pilgrims trod the marble pavements of the Temple, gaping at its awesome expanse of white and gold, they would watch Rabbi Jonathan amid his disciples or listen to him disputing with other learned men about hairsplitting details in ceremonies they had never even heard of.

Sensations of this sort were pleasing enough, but the presence of Rabbi Jonathan in the flesh was harder to live up to. It is written, "Honor thy father and thy mother." It was accordingly the rabbi's custom to make a pilgrimage to visit his mother during the month of bright flowers, when the wheat was ripening for harvest and village maidens gathered aromatic herbs for washing their hair. There was a moment between the last spring rains and the endless labor of reaping and threshing when the prospect of harvest seemed to promise abundance. Tax and tithe had not been paid; and the corners of the field, which were left for the poor, had not been deducted. The gleaners had not taken their share, nor yet the oxen whom it was forbidden to muzzle while treading the corn. Often the housewife wept when after weeks of trampling on the threshing floor, of winnowing and sifting, she saw the household grain bin, which must last her until the next time of harvest, still half empty. But while the grain stood firm and golden in the field, the vineyards ripened, and the olives swelled in size, there could be rejoicing.

It was at this time that the rabbi came home. Since
the village consisted of two-score mud-brick houses
huddled together, the Rabbi Jonathan was naturally
familiar to all. This made the burden of living up to
him a common one. The village had long possessed no
synagogue, not out of lack of devotion to the religion
of its fathers, but because no one could read the scriptures fluently in Hebrew, nor translate them for the
benefit of the rest into Aramaic. The market town
had a synagogue, but the journey to attend it ran coun-
ter to the command not to travel on the Sabbath. This
was felt to be awkward for Rabbi Jonathan and to un-
derline the careless manner in which the village habitu-
ally observed the Law.

To be sure, it did its best. For the rabbi's coming,
houses were swept, graves whitewashed, earthen
roofs rolled flat. Careless practices, such as eating in
the fields with unwashed hands, were discontinued.
Jakim bound to his doorpost a leather case containing a
strip of the Law, the only one in the village, which the
rabbi had taught him to touch as he passed and to kiss
the hand which had touched it. All little boys were
anxiously examined by their elders. Their instruction,
which was in their fathers' hands, proceeded at random
during the great part of the year. The "Hear, O Israel"
and other common prayers they knew, as well as a
number of blessing songs for the corn, rain incanta-
tions, sayings and gestures potent to avert the evil eye,
and simple habits of cleanliness, Sabbath-keeping, or
food preparation. For daily life these sufficed, but not

for the rabbi. Men rummaged their memories for texts of the Law and drove them into their sons with many beatings. To the children, the rabbi's coming was indeed no unmixed blessing.

Strangely enough, when he did come, it was with the children that the rabbi spent most time. A scrupulous Pharisee of the school of the saintly Hillel, Rabbi Jonathan honored his mother too deeply to criticize her or her household, or even those among whom she lived. His yearly visit, however, was a time of terrible penance, since it forced him to associate with those too ignorant of the fine details of God's Law to be truly pious. In fact, the rabbi felt defiled by all about him. Only the children, whose ignorance was not yet guilt in the eyes of the Lord, were welcome to him.

Accordingly, it was through the children that the real greatness of the rabbi became clear. To the elders, he had long been Law incarnate. Rabbi Jonathan, they were convinced, knew everything. All problems, all quarrels, all debts, all marriage arrangements were saved to be pronounced on by his judgment. Never did he fail to produce a Scripture quotation and to deduce from this a governing rule. To the rabbi, the loftiest principle and the smallest gesture were equally directed by the Scriptures. His life had been devoted to the extension of the Law to cover all actions which a man could conceivably perform. To the village, however, his awesome knowledge in this respect was less remarkable than the fact that he had performed an actual miracle.

When he was ten years old, the son of Miriam by the latest of her husbands was possessed by a devil. There may even have been several devils involved, since the illness, which had started by a fever and convulsions, passed eventually into a dull, settled melancholy. The boy neither spoke nor appeared to hear. He needed to be washed and dressed and fed like a baby. People said that Miriam, whose tongue was always indiscreet, had boasted too loudly that young Jacob favored his uncle. This sort of thing was bound to attract the attention of a devil to the lad, and behold the result!

When the Rabbi Jonathan came for his annual visit and was brought to see the child, he looked very grave. Such dumb devils, he said, were by no means easily cast out, while for his part, he had never had any special skill in healing. Nevertheless, for his sister's sake and trusting in the Lord, he would do what he could. The cure, however, if it were to be effective, would take time. It also needed the strictest privacy. If Miriam would leave him and the child alone in her upper room, he would try his skill.

For five days after this from the third hour of the day until the breaking of his fast at noon, Rabbi Jonathan wrestled with Jacob's stubborn devil. On the sixth day, which was the Sabbath, Jacob not only attended synagogue, but astonished his elders with the wisdom of his answers. None could guess how the miracle had been performed; and none had dared inquire, save the rabbi's other nephew, Jakim's son, who was not considered to reflect a great deal of credit on his father.

Even this young Jonas held his tongue until the rabbi
had departed for Jerusalem, taking Jacob with him,
that he might put him to the study of the Law. After-
wards, however, Jonas boasted to a friend that he had
eavesdropped on the rabbi from the roof of a nearby
house. Within an hour, the tale was all over the village.

Jakim beat his son for the look of the thing, but
everyone would have been grateful if only Jonas had
been telling the truth. But what he insisted on was so
stupid and childish that some thought he had made up
the whole story. Others said darkly that the awful in-
cantations of the rabbi were doubtless such that he did
not dare repeat them. In either case, the village was no
wiser; and Jakim gave his son another beating.

The Rabbi Jonathan, Jonas said, had been telling a
story. "And there were stalls for the beasts," the rabbi
had been saying, "and cages for the birds, both big and
little; while all the creeping things nested in the cran-
nies. How big was this ark, do you think, to contain
them all?"

There had been a silence.

"Well, I will tell you," the rabbi said. "It was as big
as our whole village with all the houses in it. And
there was hay for the cattle, and meat for the hyenas,
berries for the birds, dust for the worms, and good
wheat bread for the people, all in order. Now do you
imagine there was room for everything that the Lord
had made to inhabit the whole earth?"

Again there was silence.

"Then I will tell you," said the rabbi again. "There

was not. There was no room for the great rhinoceros
at all. You do not know the great rhinoceros? Look,
I will draw him on the ground, so that you may see
him if you but turn your head . . . That is better.
There stands the great rhinoceros, looking like this
with his nose turned up just so and a horn on his lip.
Now how big do you suppose the rhinoceros was?"

He waited a little.

"The great rhinoceros was four and a half miles long!
When you go with me on the Sabbath to the synagogue,
we will walk there and we will walk halfway back.
So far is it from here at the tip of his tail to the horn
which grows on his lip. Now, how could Noah fit
the great rhinoceros into his ark that he might not
drown?"

"If you do not know what Noah did," the rabbi
said, "you may shake your head . . . I thought you
did not. I will tell you. He made a hole in the bottom
of the ark, just so big. That looks a very large hole, but
it was only big enough for the tipmost tip of the
turned-up nose in the hole so that the rhinoceros could
breathe. They floated across the water like that with
the great rhinoceros trailing out behind the ark for
four miles and a half, while all the animals hushed up
their screams and twitters and howls and roars to listen
to the snorting sound of the great rhinoceros breathing
through his hole in the bottom of the ark."

There had been a silence for a moment or two again.
Then Jacob had laughed.

This preposterous tale gave Jonas a bad name in the

village. When Miriam's eggs were eaten by a weasel, she blamed Jonas. When Jonas and Caleb, the carpenter's son, threw stones at an owl, it was Jonas who hit the carpenter's goat instead and caused her to bring forth a dead kid. When Miriam's fig tree was stripped of the first ripe figs — and on the Sabbath, too — why, Jonas was every day in her yard. Ever since young Jacob had gone to study the Law and bring yet more glory on the village, Miriam had claimed part of Jonas's time. It always happened that the milk thistle or dandelion leaves which Jonas gathered for Miriam's salads were tough and old, her crocus corms were mixed with inedible roots, her berries gritty with earth, her fuel scanty. In fact, young Jonas was a good-for-nothing, all agreed.

Next year Rabbi Jonathan fell sick and was not able to visit his mother at the usual time, for which reason things in the village went very wrong. There had been no late rains, so that the wheat fields withered before the grain swelled in the ear. The vines, which should have been setting their fruit, were dusty and dry. The figs were scanty. Only the olives, which had put forth their myriad scented blossoms before the drought, still promised good harvest. Such a season in the village was sheer disaster. Even in good times, the living afforded by the soil was scant. In bad, there was nothing to fall back on except the moneylender in the nearby town. Once in his toils, ruin was certain. Good years could only put it off, not avert it. Already four or five had lost the ownership of their land and only tilled it on a sharecropping system — slow starvation, just endurable with the help the Law provided for the poor.

Such a future stared everyone in the face. The wild herbs on the hillsides were withering before their time. People hunted them, gathering the little pods of wild lupine or vetch, only just eatable and generally considered food for goats. Each watched his miserable harvest day and night on the threshing floor. When he brought it home at last, he buried it somewhere, fearing theft.

"If the Rabbi Jonathan were here," people said one to another, "he would bring us rain."

Everything had been done. The children had gone round the village, carrying a cock to crow for rain. The women had ground their hand mills, calling for thunder. Rain songs had been sung, charms muttered, and in secret peculiar ceremonies having very little to do with the worship of the Lord had been performed. The period of the late rains was over now. Cisterns were ominously low. Nothing but the miracle of a summer thunderstorm would save the remnant of the grapes. Even the olives — or was this imagination? — drooped a little in the clear, dry, rainless air.

Everybody's nerves were on edge. As if there were not enough to be borne, the village was troubled by a series of thefts. Some of these, perhaps, had been imaginary. People measured their grain with anxious eyes, not always allowing for the bulk made up by dried dung or stones from the threshing floor too small to be caught by the sieve. It was easy to over-estimate when so much difference was made by every handful. Yet here and there food had been snatched or articles stolen which could be disposed of in the market town for a few coppers.

There was no habitual thief in the village. Had there been one, he must have been discovered long since in so small a place. Children, however, had natures which required constant correction. Suspicion, buzzing like a fly around the village, settled on Jonas.

Jakim defended his son; but Jakim, though respected for his kinship to the rabbi, was ineffective. Miriam, who always spoke her mind, had far more influence, even with the men. Besides, a scapegoat was conveni-ent to all, since everybody was privately relieved not to be suspected.

Nothing much was done to Jonas. Was he after all not kin to the rabbi? But he came home day after day with his face cut or knocked about, his arm twisted, his bundle of brush taken by bigger boys. If he so much as went down the village street, there was muttering behind him. On the Sabbath, no one would walk with Jakim and his son to the synagogue. There was already a whisper that the Lord would withold rain until some justice was done. It only needed a little more time in which to complete the ruin of the grape harvest, and something would be done — something ugly which the village would not forget. The thefts continued.

Rabbi Jonathan arrived unannounced, dusty with walking through the withered countryside in that hot summer. Always thin, he now looked gaunt and his eyes were rimmed with red; but he had hastened to pay his respects to his mother as soon as he could bear the journey.

Jakim came out of his house with his son to greet the rabbi, whereat the people who had crowded around the great man drew back. A dead silence fell.

"Peace be with you, my brother Jakim," said the rabbi.

"A-and may thy coming be blessed." Jakim stumbled over the words of the reply, conscious of unfriendly looks and worrying also about the consequences of entertaining the rabbi from his small household store. "All that is mine is yours, my brother," he said with a simple dignity which needed no pretensions. "But the land is dry."

"All Israel is dry," the rabbi answered. "In Jerusalem, the poor will die in the streets this winter for lack of bread."

"Are there not rich men in Jerusalem to care for the poor?" cried Eleazar, who was the beekeeper. "And who have we? Rabbi Jonathan, give us rain!"

"Give us rain!"

The rabbi looked at Eleazar, who was one of those with whom he had tended the goats long ago and gathered the fuel. "The Holy One, blessed be He, gives rain," said the rabbi, drawing about him like a

cloak the dignity of an elder in Israel. "And He with-
holds it at His pleasure. I will pray for Israel." He
moved towards the house of Jakim, and no one dared
entreat him again.

Of course matters could not rest there. Rabbi Jonathan had silenced the village hothead, but nothing
whatever could silence his sister Miriam. She poured
out all the troubles of the village, the poor harvest, reports of theft, the mischievous tricks of young Jonas,
fears for the future, threats, mutterings, all so jumbled
that only one wise in the ways of the village could understand her. Perhaps the rabbi knew that even his
dignity would have no effect on his sister when she was
in one of her states. At all events, he listened to
Miriam, and later to Jakim indignantly defending his
son.

"Is Jonas a magician to steal grain more jealously
guarded than any merchant's silver? If the adze of the
carpenter is missing, what need has a boy of that? Is it
not probable that Eleazar's wife broke her own pot and
buried the fragments because she is afraid of her husband's temper? What year does Miriam not complain
of stolen figs? Is not her fig tree beside the public
street, and is my Jonas the only boy in town? Has he a
devil that he should be worse than all other boys? Do
I fail to correct him?"

It was plain that he did not. The boy Jonas, set in
punishment to turn the heavy grindstone, which was a
woman's task, had a crisscross of welts on his back. He

sat hunched over his work and did not look at the rabbi.

"Are there then no thefts after all?" asked the rabbi, wondering.

Jakim shrugged angrily. "Do they need to be blamed on my household? Must my son be stoned when he walks through the village? Is he to suffer because tempers are short? We need rain!"

"We need rain!" It was the constant cry. Jakim's house consisted of a single room which he shared with goats and hens. A raised platform provided quarters for his women. There was a ladder leading to the roof, which had a booth upon it now placed at the rabbi's disposal. But when he went up there to pray, the people gathered on the nearby roofs would hush one another. "Be quiet while the rabbi prays for rain!" Rabbi Jonathan heard them, so that the longing of the people began to come between himself and God.

"Why do they look to me for a miracle?" he complained to Jakim. "Am I not your brother, a man like themselves? What can I do?"

Jakim stared at him in surprise. "Did you not cast a devil out of Jacob?"

The rabbi's hand fingered his beard in an uncertain gesture which his pupils in the intricacies of the Law had never beheld. Single-minded always, Rabbi Jonathan had not considered the effect on the people of his rescue of Jacob, a lad too gentle to bear his mother's temper. "I made a guess," he protested to Jakim almost imploringly. "It so chances that I have seen other such devils which a man can sometimes cast out. Only the

Holy One, blessed be He, can bring rain."

"But the Holy One is with you, my brother," Jakim
pointed out.

The rabbi perceived that argument was useless, and
he fell to musing over miracles instead. There was
no situation, Rabbi Jonathan taught, out of which the
Lord could not bring good. The village people, who
were not in the habit of reflection, had not noticed any
change in the boy Jonas. He was obstinate and sullen,
which was what they expected him to be. It was only
the rabbi who remembered Jonas as a lively boy,
though with too great a love of idle mischief.

On the Sabbath afternoon, Rabbi Jonathan gathered
the people on the village threshing floor, which was
their meeting place, since they had no market square
in which they could assemble. Here he reminded them
of how it was written in the Scriptures, "Thou shalt
not steal." Times were hard, and some of the village
had sinned against this law. Let them confess it, lest
the anger of the Lord persist against His people.

There was a muttering. Men nudged their neighbors and looked at young Jonas. Under the gaze of the
rabbi, however, nothing was said.

Rabbi Jonathan rose to his full impressive height and
stood looking down on the people, his tall figure outlined by the declining sun. "If the guilty will not
speak," he said, "I shall denounce him."

This time there was complete and awful silence.

"So be it," said the rabbi. He began to walk around
the circle of his neighbors, stopping as he came to the

head of every household. Without a word, he put into each man's hand a single straw. When he came to Jakim, however, he shook his head. "Here is a man without guile, nor does it become me to accuse the son of my mother." Passing by Jakim, he gave the straw to Jonas, completing the circle.

"Now every man has a piece of straw," said the rabbi. "And all these straws I have cut to the same length. You have asked for a miracle, and I will give you such a one as I can perform. Next Sabbath day at this time, each man shall bring me back his straw. Then if any be guilty, either himself or his household, his straw will have grown longer by the width of my little fingernail."

For the following week, there was turmoil in the village. If the head of the household had a conscience clear as day, he was still forced to make inquiry among his women and children, lest he be shamed next Sabbath in front of the whole village. Many questions were asked, and some beatings were given; but no man would measure his straw by his neighbors or admit guilt.

The only household which remained at peace that week was that of Jakim, who had been given no straw. No one questioned Jonas, and his sullen silence was accepted as usual. But in the quiet of the night or the gray of the morning when everyone was asleep, the boy looked at his straw.

There was always a lamp alight in Jakim's house, the wick just floating in a small measure of oil. This was not extravagance on Jakim's part, but the cheapest way of keeping fire alight, since kindling methods were uncertain and brushwood hard to come by. Jonas could hold up his straw in the dimness and try to measure it with the stretch of his hand. Had it grown or not? He was never certain, but his conscience was heavy.

He ought to have let the figs of his aunt Miriam alone . . . He had only meant to play a trick on her by eating a few. It was the early crop, and there had not been so many on the tree. He had not intended . . .

Now everybody would know, and the rabbi would blame him for other wrong things which he had not done. Every night Jonas examined that straw. He thought; he was half-sure; he was finally certain that it was longer. In desperation, he took out his knife, measured very exactly the width of a fingernail, and cut it off. But his misery, which should have been relieved, became almost too acute to bear. There was no lifting of the burden of his guilt, which only terror had prevented him confessing long since. In the silence of the night, Jonas shed tears.

The week went slowly by, and Sabbath day came round again. All assembled, some shamefaced and some stern. But when the rabbi called on the guilty to speak, there was no answer.

"So be it," the rabbi said. In dignified silence he went around to every man, collecting his straw. Deliberately he took each back to his seat and laid it beside him, matching it against the rest. When he had quite done, there was an awful silence. The people sat waiting. The hand of the rabbi, which should have been outstretched in denunciation, went with that uncertain gesture to his beard. Beside him lay all the straws in a row, but every one of them was of exactly equal length.

The Rabbi Jonathan moistened his lips with his tongue; but before he spoke, he took inward counsel with the Lord. The continued silence was too much for young Jonas. He burst into tears.

"I did it," he wept. "I did take Miriam's figs. And I was frightened because my straw had grown. So I cut it off!"

There was a muttering. People reminded one another what they had always said about the boy. But the rabbi, getting up again and towering over them all with anger in his face cried, "Silence!" All grew still.

"You fools!" the rabbi said. "Am I the Holy One that I should make a straw grow which is dried, cut, and dead? No, by your consciences I know you. Everyone who knew his secret guilt has cut his straw — as this boy did. And behold, each straw is still of the same length!"

The village took in very slowly what the rabbi was saying. There were whisperings and shakings of the head. Each turned from his neighbor and, fearing to look at the rabbi, gazed on the ground.

"You hypocrites!" the rabbi cried, terrible in his indignation. "Did you not put your own sins on this poor boy, the only one among you with the courage

to confess? Tell me, therefore, what shall be done to a
wicked generation? How shall the Lord come to a
reckoning with you? For you are of the chosen, the
seed of Israel, and are bound by God's Law."

No one had anything to say. To the rabbi, gentle
by nature, no punishment presented itself which was
fitting for their sin. But Jakim, getting up and raising
Jonas with him, lifted his mild eyes to heaven and said,
"Shall carelessness or injustice come between neighbors? If so, then each man stands alone. Let us all pray
for rain."

I ✱
SEE

IT WAS the middle of the day, and Galilee drowsed in the sun. Out on the dusty hills the shepherds and their flocks sought patches of shade amid the scattered trees or thorny scrub. In the little stone-walled vine-yards where the grapes were ripening for harvest, watchmen snored in their summer shelters. Down in the village, the noise of the grindstones was still, the clatter of voices hushed. No one was moving along the dusty road which led through the market place and down into Capernaum on the lakeside. Even the beg-gar had felt his way with the ease of age-long practice into the shade of the nearest wall, where he slept, a heap of rags.

He was not the small town's only beggar. There was also the cripple at the other end of the market and the idiot gaping at vacancy outside the synagogue, too stupid to move across the road out of the sun. There were also the poor, the half-starved families of the day laborers in richer men's vineyards. Yet whereas others were spoken of by name with a hint of scornful pity, this man only was referred to by young and old as sim-ply, "the beggar." It was a tribute not merely to the length of time he had practiced his trade, but to his character.

He was five years old when he had lost his sight, and ten when his father had died, leaving his mother to eke out what sort of living she could by helping other housewives in return for a piece of bread or a rag of clothing. Similar refuse with a few scattered coins fell to the lot of the beggar, and on this they had lived some thirty years. The people of the town were not unkind, but cash was hard to come by. Nothing edible was ever bestowed without pain. The purpose of begging by immemorial custom was to tap some of the wealth which flowed through the village on its way from the uplands down to Capernaum. This might have been well, had the trade of Capernaum primarily gone that way; but as it happened, few of the travelers had much to spare. Besides, when there were beggars in every village, even a kindly man grew tired of giving. For all these reasons, the mere survival of this beggar for a generation was a respectable feat.

He had not lived well. To look at, he was a bundle of bones, the knobby joints standing out on sticklike arms and on legs which seemed only just able to support the rest of him without absolutely breaking. Yet, as some travelers found to their cost, he was very tenacious and could cling to a man or his ass like a burr, not to be dislodged save by force. Not every passerby, however, received this treatment. The beggar was able to detect by the very footsteps of a man or the trotting of his ass whether a traveler was good for alms or a blow and whether pity or outright violence would work on him.

He had long ago learned every footstep in the village. He knew exactly how often to let each one pass with "pity the poor beggar," and when to screech until the women came running to their doors and the victim, shamefaced, parted with some small gift. In fact, so moderate were his demands that the regularity with which he exacted his tributes escaped notice. Most people gave readily enough because they knew that thereafter he really would let them alone. Nor did they fancy to have their secrets yelled abroad.

From long practice, the hearing of the beggar was very acute. It was surprising how much that was said, even within doors, he had heard and remembered. In fact, there were skills to the beggar's trade, and this man had mastered them all. The state of the harvest, the weather, the mood of the man who came by, his nationality and probable business must be considered. Every waking moment in these many years the beggar had devoted to snatching the pittance he needed not only from the wealthy, the kindhearted, and the pious, but from the churlish and the grudging. Even now, at siesta time, he slept as an old dog sleeps, twitching slightly, ready to spring to his feet at the pad of a footstep.

A man came down the road, a man in a hurry, since he traveled in the heat, and for the same reason a young man and not rich. By the length of his stride, he was an upland man, and by the firmness of it one in good health and cheerful, but not burdened by any sort of baggage. All this the beggar knew before an

onlooker would have supposed him awake. Bag of
bones though he already was, he shrank together, knees
bent, head trembling, fingers stretched like claws. No
inch of him but presented a terrible contrast to the
youth and strength approaching. The beggar knew
how to play on a man's pride as well as his weakness.
Even a rustic would have some food about him. The
countryside was now between harvests, so that today
he had taken nothing. A single raisin or the wild
fruits gathered by the poor were worth a performance.

"Lord, Lord," moaned the beggar, the very sinews
of his neck standing out with seeming effort to speak
above a dying whisper. "Have pity on a poor beggar!"
He heard the footsteps stop and groaned faintly, far
too clever to spoil his own effect by further insistence.

A voice said quietly, "Thy sins be forgiven thee!"
And the footsteps passed on.

The beggar's mouth dropped open, and for a moment he was bereft of speech, which had not happened since very long ago when he had discovered that
anything was better than starvation. What an extraordinary thing to say! He was literally rooted to the
spot with sheer astonishment. In fact, the footsteps
were fading away before it came to him in a slow flood-
ing of rage what the phrase meant. "Thy sins be forgiven thee!" He had no sins.

After all, what had he ever done but beg, as he had
been forced to do since before he was of an age to be
accountable. Had he ever stolen, lied (save in the way
of business), done harm to any man? Crouching like

an old, blind, toothless dog at the village gate, what could he do? Had he not, unlike the village cripple, shared with his mother his miserable gains? If he had not, indeed, blind and helpless as he was, how could he have lived? Nor was the Law of the Holy One on his conscience. He said his "Hear, O Israel," and the synagogue elders in pious charity paid his Temple tax. He knew he was but dirt in their eyes — yet many provisions of the Law he need not carry out because of his blindness. Others his poverty made impossible. In Galilee and among the poor, what a man could not do was never counted against him. The beggar kept the Sabbath. He went to the synagogue. Otherwise, he must have starved long since. A village beggar must always study to be thought deserving.

He had never felt insulted before. He accepted abuse as his due. Eagles soared, goats leaped, worms crawled. Men, too, were rich, poor, destitute. They sat on thrones. They lay in the dirt. Each had his degree, and that of the beggar was lowest of all. It was natural for men to revile him, since his position was vile. But no one had ever laid sin to his door. How could he sin?

The more the beggar brooded, the angrier he grew. He had been taken so entirely by surprise that he had not attempted to get his own back on that man. It galled him terribly that he had not been able to think of one wounding thing to say, he who had studied so many ways of making people squirm. And now it was too late. Nobody would have seen that traveler come down the street at siesta time, except the idiot drooling in the sun, too hot to have slept. He might even pass by on his way back and not be recognized. The beggar ground his teeth at the thought of being inspected by that man's eyes again without even knowing. He had nothing but the confident footsteps to go by, and that calm voice. "Thy sins be forgiven thee!" Would he ever forget it?

He did not forget it. During the long hours when he necessarily sat idle, a slow fire burned in him, fed by his resentment at having been taught to bear malice. When he had fastened cruel nicknames on the meanest men in town or had shouted the shame of their private dealings to people at large, he had merely done so because, if he had not, they never would have feared him enough to give him alms. This was their nature, while to extract something from them against their will was his profession. He had neither liked, nor yet disliked them while he did it. But now his self-respect was actually damaged because he wanted revenge. He would not be whole again until he got it.

Perhaps the footsteps often passed this way, or perhaps they never came. The beggar could not be sure; but listening for them, he felt he was losing his touch. He may have been so, though times were also getting harder and people were hardening, too. At all events, the beggar had bad luck. His mother, grown shrewish with hardship and old age, screamed at him for a lazy good-for-nothing. All of this in his mind

stemmed not so much from the insult, as from his pow-
erlessness to answer the man.

When the footsteps came at last, they were in company, so that he did not know them. It was only the
calm voice he recognized as it said to his companions,
"That tree is barren, and it will always be so."

The beggar gathered himself together and leaped,
knocking someone aside and clawing for the mantle
which he knew must be there. "O thou!" screeched
the beggar at the top of his voice, "thou who canst forgive sin, now heal my blindness!"

Two people fought to tear him off; but the beggar,
engrossed in the scene he had prepared so long, was
not to be shaken. Twisting himself inside a fold of
the mantle and clinging as though for dear life, he
went on screaming, "Now heal me, forgiver of sins!
Now heal my blindness!"

"Let him go," the quiet voice said. Still clinging,
lest his victim escape, the beggar stopped screaming.
He had expected to put his enemy to ignominious
flight. Few liked a scene. However, if excuses were
now to be offered in the vain hope of placating him, it
would cost nothing to hear them out. The soul of the
beggar was drinking that for which it had been athirst,
and he wanted to drain the last drop down.

No excuses were given. The man bent over and
put his hands across the eyes of the beggar, those red
and tortured eyeballs, long corroded by the dust that
had eaten them away. Then after a minute, he took
his hands off and said, "Now, see!"

For a dazzling split second, the blind beggar looked up into the eyes of the healer. Then as it dawned upon his senses that he in fact did see, he shrieked in terror and buried his face in his hands. Vaguely he heard the men go on, but he would not have stopped them, even had his head not reeled and his ears rung. That any witchcraft could as it were have opened that instant vision, that flash of illusion, was a horrifying thing. A man's face, indistinct and swimming before him in a mist of his own tears! A dazzle of light! He would rather have been quietly blind from birth than smitten by this terrible second of sight.

There were still tears in his eyes. His hands were wet. He took them away, blinked at them . . . and saw again. Throbbingly like circulation cut off and restored, the consciousness flooded through him that he indeed did see. He shrieked again and scrambled up out of the dust onto his sticklike legs that wobbled beneath him. He was dizzy. Things were whirling, shapes undefined, light dazzling, nothing comprehended but the central fact of all. "I see! I see!"

Townspeople, indifferent, hitherto, to the noise made by their beggar over a stranger passing through, came running out. He was staggering up the dusty street, his hands clawing the air as they had so often done for alms, his red eyes glaring, his head turning from side to side, as he screeched like a madman, "I see! I *see!* I SEE!"

People thought he really was mad at first, and only the stronger of those who were not in the fields would venture to approach him. One of these brought rope.

"No, no!" cried the beggar, shrinking away. In a confused manner, he caught the need for some explanation; but the experience was too tremendous to be compressed into thought or shaped into words. He could only say quiveringly again, "I see! I see!"

"The man does see!" cried Susannah, quicker of thought than the men. "Stand back from him! Joseph, son of Eleazar, what do I hold in my hand?"

Joseph, son of Eleazar, never hitherto addressed by his full name, peered at Susannah, whose figure was blended with a kaleidoscope of bright colors all running together in his mind. Trembling with a visible effort so great that nobody spoke, he stood for a few minutes, wide eyes wandering from side to side, as though they could not focus, do what he would. Then, putting his hand to his lips and stretching it slowly from there toward Susannah, he opened his mouth and said hesitatingly, "It is a distaff . . . with a hank of wool upon it. I can see!"

"He can see! It is a miracle!" More people swarmed out into the street or ran to their doorways, staring puzzled at the shouting crowd around the beggar. With a common impulse, everybody had to touch him, seize his hands, pat his shoulder. Children skirmished around the outsides of the group or ran home, yelling, "It is a miracle! Our beggar can see!"

Joseph, son of Eleazar, tottered as he was pushed and pulled by too great kindness. His mouth hung open;

tears rolled down his cheeks; he struggled alike for breath and for coherence.

"Leave me . . . !" he pushed and pawed unavailingly. "Friends, leave me . . . at least my rags." His threadbare garments were parting under the strain, and there was danger that he would in a moment or two be almost naked.

Already Susannah had rushed away to bring forth not her husband's Sabbath garments, but a worn set, still very good, which was awaiting another few inches of growth from her eldest son. Pushing through the crowd, and helped by eager hands about her, she thrust the outer garment over his shoulders, piling the others into his astonished arms. "A miracle! Blessed be the Holy One," cried Susannah, panting. "And blessed be he in whom the power of the King of Kings is manifested!"

"Blessed be he! Blessed be He!" One man brought a pair of sandals, another a goat's-milk cheese, another wine. This last was agreed to be an inspiration. Celebration was called for, and the very nearness of the grape harvest justified a small extravagance. Even those prudent, saving people who did not display to their neighbors how much they actually had, brought out unexpected riches for the mere pleasure of holding them up in the beggar's sight and shouting, "What do you see?"

There was a moment's pause when old Joanna, with yelling little boys turning cartwheels or jumping

up and down in sheer excitement, came hobbling down
the street at an almost-run. When she saw her son with
his new garment about him and gifts piled high at his
feet, she would not even touch him, but stood three
paces off. Tears rolled down her wrinkled cheeks,
and her mouth worked, but she said nothing.

"Who is she?" asked the beggar, who had not seen
his mother since he was a child of five and she a tall, fair
woman.

At that, his mother cried out in her old cracked voice
so that he knew her and beheld one startled glance what
the years had done to her. He stepped out and took
her in his arms. They clung together, both weeping
for the hunger, the cold, the despair which had embittered their lives, making her a scold and him a burden.

It was not possible to remember such things very
long in a crowd of people intent on merrymaking. Already the cymbals and the castanets for dancing had
been brought out. The place for a party was here and
everywhere, in the streets, in the yards of the people.
Spaces were cleared of clutter, water brought out for
washing of hands. A festive garment was found for
Joanna, too; and her feet were guided to an honorable seat in one of the wealthier houses where she
had drudged at the handmill often enough.

That day passed like a dream. Unaccustomed to
either good food or wine, the head of the beggar was
very soon swimming with an added confusion. This
actually pleased the crowd, who were content to carry

him home in procession and to go on celebrating the
miracle without him. Wild stories were current already about how a heavenly angel had been sent on
purpose from the Holy One, blessed be He. For both
the people and the beggar himself had been too stunned
by the event to pay much attention to the manner in
which it had been brought about.

This situation was rectified the following morning.
The elders of the synagogue, responsible for what
went on in town, were by no means happy that an angel
of the Most High should appear to a beggar when those
who studied God's Law saw no such thing. In fact,
since angels of the Lord were quite uncommon and
miracle workers less so, they saw no reason to suppose
too rashly that the Lord had performed this wonder.
Many magicians of the Chaldaeans or the Egyptians, for
instance, were known to have done strange things with
the aid of their devils.

Questioned, the beggar told an unsatisfactory story.
He did not know the healer, was not even certain that
he would recognize him if he met him. He had been
bearded, dark, not ordinary-looking, yet possessed of a
nose and eyes and mouth in no way peculiar. He had
been a son of Abraham, since he wore earlocks. This
description was confirmed by various people who had
noticed the little group passing down the street, but
had paid small attention, distracted by the behavior of
the beggar. John, son of Hanan, who was one of the
town's rich men and sold in Capernaum the produce of
his flocks and of his vineyards, now mentioned that

there was a preacher in that place with powers of healing.

The elders of the synagogue looked sour. Pressed
for more details, the beggar had been ashamed to account for his motives in appealing to be cured. He
had said vaguely that he did not know, supposed that
it must have been an inspiration. Asked whether the
healer had invoked the Holy One or a devil, he could
remember neither.

All in all, the people of the town were free to inter-
pret the miraculous cure as they pleased. So also
were the elders, who sternly impressed on the beggar
that he was hardly worthy of divine interposition. Let
him, however, praise God and give a thank-offering
from among his new possessions. Having in this fashion
taken both sides at once, they dismissed him with a
warning to behave himself in future.

In this way, some enthusiasm was damped, though
by no means all. The beggar did see. The cripple,
who undertook a slow and painful journey into Capernaum, came limping back, disappointed, bearing news
that the healer had removed across the lake into the
territory of Philip the Tetrarch. He did not fail to
detract from his rival's good fortune by claiming that
in Capernaum itself far greater wonders, even to the
raising of the dead, had come to pass. As he rapidly
perceived, a slight disappointment was already being
felt by those very people who had been the foremost
to salute the miracle. Meanwhile, however, the ap-

proach of the grape harvest prolonged celebrations by giving the annual festival new excitement.

Joseph, son of Eleazar, now raised officially to the dignity of his own name throughout the township, and indeed for a radius of some ten miles, did his best to be a worthy hero. Unquestionably, however, now that his eyes were opened, he gave the impression of being half-witted. People who had marveled at his quickness in recognizing footsteps, could not understand that faces all looked alike to his unaccustomed eyes. In fact, the concentration which had produced his former acuteness was shattered, while his new perceptions were too varied to be sorted out. From the very first, questions about what he saw had produced confusion in him. Gradually his interrogators, losing their earlier awe, began to sharpen their wits at his expense.

For some time Joseph himself did not discover this. In his own opinion, he was learning strange new things at extraordinary speed. Aware, moreover, that he still remained the focus of far more attention than he had ever known, he was not sensitive to a change in the quality of public interest. His simple story was still in demand. Contributions from the countryside flowed in, though at diminishing speed. Since the harvest was the most abundant in years, people were rejoicing in the unaccustomed pleasures of being liberal. Better clothed, better fed, used to a hand-to-mouth existence, it did not occur to Joseph that his present life was but a bridge between his past and a perilous future.

His mother opened his eyes by losing her temper with him in her old habitual fashion.

"You shiftless dog!" she screamed at him on returning from a gossip at the well to find her son still lying on the new mat which now formed his bedding. "You worthless bag of bones! You good-for-nothing! How long will you sit idle while your old mother drudges?"

"What else should I do?" inquired Joseph, mildly surprised. Since their prosperity, his mother had been gentle, almost subdued. It did not please him that she should take her old tone again. Besides, she had roused him from contemplation of a spider repairing her web. It often happened that the act of seeing would occupy his time for hours together without any conscious thoughts being present in his mind. On this occasion, he did not so much as turn his head to look at Joanna.

"Work!" cried Joanna, delivering an angry box on his ear. "Are you a baby that you should open your mouth and be fed? Go out and work!"

He sat up in surprise. "I cannot beg now."

"Who talked of begging? Do not other men labor?"

"But . . ."

She lifted quivering hands to heaven. "What sin is there in me that I should have borne a worthless son? Was it ever the custom that when a man is well, he should do nothing? Already the neighbors gossip about your idle ways."

In all the days of his blindness, it had never once occurred to Joseph to do any more than endure his mother's anger. But now his open hand, without any volition of his own, caught her in the mouth. For a moment after the slap, there was utter silence, he still sitting, she stooped over, staring at him above her hand. Then she burst into tears. "It only needed this! To strike his mother! A devil is in him."

Perhaps a devil was, thought Joseph, plunging out into the street, almost as much astonished as dismayed. He himself was not to blame for what had happened. How could he ever in his own right senses have lifted his hand against his mother? Yet if Joanna did not hold her tongue, what would now become of him? Indistinctly there loomed for the first time a terrifying future in which he was neither an object of charity nor a living example of divine favor to the righteous.

"God be with you!" It was Elias, Susannah's husband, who put himself in Joseph's way. It was a terrible effort to recognize the man and, having done so, to greet him as if nothing were the matter.

"And may your coming be blessed," Joseph replied. Unhappily, Elias did not pass on, but turned, accommodating his pace to Joseph's own.

"There is a little matter . . ."

Joseph, who was used to this approach, put out his hand; but the other pressed nothing into it. In fact, he did not seem to notice the gesture.

"It is . . . er . . ." he began. "Well, the grape harvest is over and . . . as Susannah says . . . er . . . She was talking about your return of the loan of our son's garments. He is our eldest and growing tall by now, while the second is big enough to need his Sabbath clothes. Susannah wondered . . ."

"You shall have them," Joseph said in a strained, hoarse voice, "tomorrow."

"Oh, no hurry!" Elias sounded taken aback. "But Susannah says . . ."

"Tomorrow." Joseph quickened his pace almost to a run. He knew now where he was going — where he had to go. Day laborers offered themselves for hire in a corner of the market. It was already the third hour of the day and too late to hope for full employment. Luckless people, however, waited patiently for casual work, an hour of hauling or some vile task which better folk avoided. After the harvest, there were always some who all day long got nothing.

It was several days before he actually found courage to range himself with those he had been watching. His reception was not friendly. None of the laborers desired more competition, especially from Joseph, whose reputation would recommend him to employers.

"Look at that bag of bones," said one with a coarse laugh.

"He do a day's work!" agreed another, clapping Joseph so heavily on the shoulder that he staggered. "He'll never last."

This was the private opinion of hirers of labor, who wanted men for straightening up the tangle of the vineyards, repairing walls which had been knocked about, taking down the watchmen's shelters, and piling the brush of which they were composed for firewood. Such tasks needed a rugged physical strength, the more so as summer was now at its hottest and the rains not yet expected. The town, however, agreed that Joseph's action in setting out to work had been the correct one. The approval which he had begun to lose was at once restored. No doubt the Holy One would endow him with a strength which belied his appearance.

John, son of Hanan, the first to give Joseph employment, was a hard man who took no more account of his laborers than of his ass. Almost immediately, Joseph's hands were bleeding, his weak muscles racked, his poor heart pounding. Never for an instant could he make a pretence of keeping up with his fellows. Having contracted to pay for a day's work, John was determined to get it by bullying or blows. Despairing efforts, reinforced by such persuasion, kept Joseph going until siesta time. When this was over, he could not stagger to his feet. He received no sympathy. The laborers agreed that he had never done a decent day's work in his life and was now shirking. An hour or so later when he struggled into the field, John sent him roughly packing amid cruel laughter.

This ended Joseph's attempts to find work and lost him favor with rich and poor alike. The word went round that he was a good-for-nothing, as his mother, who should know best, had always called him. By now the miracle was sunk into a commonplace, some even going so far as to suggest that he had faked his blindness, recovering his sight when he thought it would bring profit.

Since Joseph could neither work nor beg, he must steal. How else could he possibly live? For the moment, the olives were swelling and, being more scattered than the vines, were not easily guarded. If one went hunting the wild bees' nests amid blossoming thyme on the hills or collecting the large black locusts considered edible by the very poor, there were opportunities for snatching unripe olives about which Joanna had the sense to keep her mouth shut. The coming of the rains and the olive harvest would put an end to all this, while on that occasion he might not receive the relief traditionally given to those who could not support themselves by their work.

For a short time, Joseph held out thus; but nowadays the future pressed on him with a desperate weight. The loss of his humble but assured place had destroyed the resignation with which he had once taken luck as it came. A taste of prosperity had exaggerated by contrast his dread of privation.

John, son of Hanan, preyed on his mind waking and sleeping. It was John's custom to pay off his men at the end of the day. The money to do so was actually carried in the fields on John's own person and must have been with him from the moment he left his own house in the gray of the morning to snap up the likeliest men in the labor market. It was not, to be sure, very much. Still, it represented a chance to get even with John and acquire a nest egg. Security for only ten days was as tempting to Joseph as a single cup of water in the midst of a desert.

In the end, he found a club and waited in an alley past which John always came on his way to the market. Remembering John's own stick across his back, it was unexpectedly easy to strike hard. But while he was stooping over his victim, fumbling with the girdle at his waist, a shout was raised behind him. Terrified, yet unwilling to lose the proceeds of his crime, he delayed for a second. Then, scrambling to his feet without his stick, he set off running, even as excited yells were re-echoed from housetops. "A thief! This way! Stop, thief!" In another moment, people would come swarming down like angry bees.

There was only one desperate chance, and he took it, fleeing down the alley toward the open fields surrounding the village. A dark figure loomed ahead. There was no side-stepping possible. He shouted, gesturing, "Ahead! Ahead! Down there! Quick, follow after!"

"Ahead!" echoed the man before him, plunging at right angles down the twisting lane where Joseph pointed. Gasping with tremendous effort, he dashed for freedom.

He was free indeed, he reflected a few hours later. In his girdle lay a dozen copper coins. Behind him waited the forty stripes less one which the synagogue elders had power to impose. If it happened that John, son of Hanan, was dead, worse would follow —

the prisons of Herod Antipas, an execution. His face
and his figure, now known to the whole district, might
at any time be recognized even in Capernaum. Past and
future had nothing in common any more. One life was
over.

He felt neither sorrow nor regret, neither guilt nor
repentance. There was nobody, not even his mother,
whose loss caused a pang. For John, son of Hanan, he
cared no more than for all those many people he had
shamed or blackmailed out of small sums. He had done
what he must to a man who had deserved robbing. Indeed, thievery, being a species of preying on others,
was more congenial to his beggar's mind than he had
any idea of. Timidity and physical feebleness might
prevent him from setting up as a brigand; but in his
vision of the future honest work had no place. One
episode had ended that. He knew no trade and was
not fit for heavy labor. But he had some money in
his girdle, and he felt the exhilaration of a man whose
dreaded moment is at last upon him. In feverish excitement which was very close to relief, he started to plan.

It was almost time for the Day of Atonement and
the joyous Festival of Booths which followed. Like
trickling streams which fed a river, scattered pilgrims
from the far corners of the earth were on their way
toward Jerusalem. Already they were passing through
Galilee, attracting others from every town until the
whole world seemed on the move. Amid such throngs,
an extra traveler would be of small account, especially
if he could join some village group with a plausible

story. Perhaps he had fallen sick and had been left behind by his friends. Recovering, he might have found his provisions for the journey had been looted. In Jerusalem, he would pretend to seek his own townsfolk out and would take farewell of those whose pious charity had helped him on his way. He might even take more than mere farewell . . . It should be easy.

It was easy. People were trusting. They even pressed on him some small amends for his supposed loss, so that during the festivals he did not need to steal. For a short period, he could stand poised between his past and his future, having no place in the world and no relationship to his fellows. To his careless vision, they still all looked alike. What held him spellbound was the holy city itself, from the very first moment when it burst on his distant gaze, its limestone battlements gold in the setting sun, its marble palaces and the Temple of the Holy One dead white. The masses of the pilgrims, the bustle in the streets, the temporary encampments outside the walls affected him only in that they afforded him cover. The fulfillment of his life had nothing to do with his fellows. Even in the vast outer court of the Temple, his gaze passed unseeing over the money changers, sellers of offerings, amateur prophets, guards, sightseeing gentiles who gave the place the air of a great market, as if worship itself were a social business.

It was not so to Joseph, who entered the Temple as a separate drop in a vast stream steadily flowing through the Beautiful Gate, where only the chosen people of God had right of entry. Swelling with wonder and awe, he gazed at the sanctuary, which towered high and square above him, flashing with gold. Before him the great altar smoked, while priests in tall white miters passed unhurriedly to and fro, each serving in his appointed order. The Levites sung heartrending music, and silver trumpets bade the people make their prostrations. The whole pageant was confused, yet familiar, the stuff of his childhood dreams, the subject of returned pilgrims' tales. Yet though a part of his entire life, it was a vision incomprehensible in splendor and glory. How could Joseph compare this Temple with the whitewashed synagogue or the mud-brick houses on which his eyes had closed and been reopened? What had the golden raiment of the High Priest to do with mere clothing?

Never was his separateness from other men more complete than at the Feast of the Atonement. At the climax of the service, two white goats were brought out, one for sacrifice, the other a scapegoat destined to bear away the people's sins. On this one the High Priest placed his hands, confessing in the presence of them all the sins of Israel. Each man, meanwhile, prostrate before the Lord, confessed his own.

Many men had tears in their eyes as each spoke privately to God; but Joseph, son of Eleazar, said nothing of sin. Once blind, he saw the glory of God. All his days unclean, he now stood ritually pure in the Temple of Israel. How should mere sin concern him? Could it increase the infinite distance between a beggar in the dust and the King of Kings? As lowliest he came to the Highest, as blind to the All-Seeing, and as mortal to the Eternal. Yet he came because called, because healed, because one of God's chosen. Surely awe and wonder were befitting, not repentance.

The High Priest, divested now of his golden raiment, took the incense which burned on the golden shovels; and holding it, he went up through the great gates into the sanctuary. Crossing the Holy Place, he passed behind the curtain into the Holy of Holies, bearing with him the nation of Israel into the presence of God. With him almost in a dream went the soul of Joseph, in a great company yet still alone, as though his blindness had drawn a fence around him, even in heaven.

But if Jerusalem was heaven, it was also hell. The Vale of the Cheesemakers, crammed between hills, was the working-class quarter, straggling like an untidy drainage ditch between the houses or palaces of the rich and the great Temple. The festivals went by. The pilgrims departed. The temporary encampments outside the walls were cleared away. The Cheesemakers' Valley remained, rough, filthy, noisy, devoid of human kindness. There were beggars here, but the patient arts of Joseph made no impression. The prizes went to sheer clamor, to skillful fakery of disgusting sores, to struggles with literal tooth and nail against rival beggars. Nor was the working part of the quarter any better. Joseph had but to open his mouth to be known as a Galilean and to be hustled, cheated, or abused. Jerusalemites were quicker of speech than he, quicker of thought. He was not a match for them, even had they not been many and he alone.

It was their appalling indifference which terrified him. At home in the village, men might not have cared if he died, but they would have noticed. He might have been without friends, but he did have neighbors. Here when a poor man fell dead in the street, the only problem was who should remove his corpse from the holy city. No one had asked him to come in the first place or cared for his going.

He had lost his place in the world, and he found no other. He could not live long in Jerusalem by stealing. He simply lacked the skill. Yet hunger and misery drove him on. The rains were beginning, and the nights were growing cold. Terrified and desperate, he snatched like a city waif, dreading each episode, yet never able to find any other way to avoid starvation.

It was one of the clear, cool nights of winter with frost in the air and an orange moon rising from behind the mountains of Moab. The homeless huddled between the corners of buildings, gathering their rags about them. Each had a favorite spot, his own by right of usage; yet there was a movement of those who, washed out of one refuge, sought another. Into the alleys, mostly dark, fell patches of moonlight. In one of these sat a beggar. Joseph, lurking in the closed doorway of a shop, watched him idly, seeing him fumble in his girdle for the coins that he had taken. He began to pass these from hand to hand, rubbing his fin-

gertips across them in an exploring gesture which
Joseph from his own blind days remembered. As he
did so, the moonlight caught one, which glistened
palely, yet unmistakably silver.

Silver! Joseph had not owned such a coin since he
came to the city. Fool of a blind man sitting in bright
moonlight and thinking it dark! Ah, food — and more
than food, a little respite from the need to snatch and
run with his heart in his mouth!

To think was to act. Without any conscious plan,
Joseph leaped. In the scuffle, the silver coin fell out
of the beggar's hand and rolled beyond his reach.
Joseph tore himself away to pick it up.

"May you become blind in your turn," yelled the
beggar after him. "See then what it is like to live! May
the Lord teach you!"

It was easy to get out of earshot. Joseph settled himself down a long way off, the coin tucked safely in his
girdle, warmed by the struggle, and farther from starving than he had been in months. A piece of silver! At
this low ebb, at last his luck had turned.

So he told himself, but to no avail. The outraged cry
of the beggar rang in his ears, "May you become blind
in your turn!" The knowledge of blindness was part
of his whole being which no act of healing could erase.
It represented his one sure place in a terrible world. In
robbing a blind man, he had done something the
enormity of which he understood. He felt, indeed, as
though he had robbed himself. Nothing to which he
could ever sink would be worse degradation than this

act, almost unplanned, as much of an impulse as when
he raised his hand against his mother. But this time he
did not lay the blame on a devil. He shivered as the
cold stole over him, and he wondered numbly what
sort of man he was that he could not even spare himself.

It did not seem to matter what he did any more.
When the silver trumpets of the Temple woke the city,
Joseph walked among the markets with his stolen coin
in his hand. But what he bought with it was not food,
but a sharp knife.

Life was easier after that, though more dangerous.
Sometimes there was blood on the knife, sometimes
not. He preyed on his own kind like a starving rat,
often taking nothing or thinking himself well off with
a copper or two.

In the end, it was the knife that destroyed him,
that and his accent. A whisper went through the un-
derworld about the Galilean. The vast indifference of
the quarter, penetrated at last, turned into enmity. It
was easier to betray him than to stick a dagger into his
ribs. It was safer, also.

Justice was slow, but the end inevitable. Joseph
looked for nothing but death. He might even have
welcomed it, had he not feared torment, since prison
was of all his experiences the least tolerable. It threw
him with other desperate people, none of whom seemed
to be dropping out of sight, like a stone into a dark well.
Hoping or despairing, they chattered endlessly of
those who loved them or of influences which might

help. In fact, the terrible indifference of Jerusalem toward himself was contrasted with the intense concern which other people appeared to arouse or feel without an effort. It dawned on Joseph that he had been better off as the blind beggar with the shrewish mother, the lowliest person in a small, fly-bitten town, but still possessing the right to wring his tribute from all comers. In his loneliness, he even descended to the humiliation of talking about himself, only to discover that fellow prisoners preferred to recount their own stories about the miracles they knew. In fact, no one cared to make a new friend, or even an enemy. In their extremities, people were only concerned with the effect of their misfortunes on those they knew already.

In the dank Roman prison to which they transferred him at last, he faced death in torment, divided from it by nothing but a short space of time. He passed the whole of this in a state of sickening dread. There was another robber with him, Levi, son of Judas, one of those zealots who killed in the name of the King of Kings and died cursing. With the brutal courage of such a man, Joseph had nothing in common. He had no cause to sustain him, no friends to distract him, no grief, no loss, no hope of being remembered. Retreating to the farthest corner of their common cell, he sat there in silence, the eyes which had cost him so much fixed on vacancy, his whole being tingling in anticipation of the long agony of dying.

When they dragged them out at last, they added a third man, a preacher whom they had tortured, so that

their procession was slow. If there had been a hundred
to die beside Joseph, he would not have turned his head
to look at them. But the preacher won him a few mo-
ments of untormented life, so that his presence was
welcome.

The endurance of agony is a private thing. The
agony of Joseph on his cross was affected by the small
crowd and the guard of soldiers as it was by the buzzing flies. They distracted the concentration of his
whole being, so that of all he had to endure, they were
in a fashion the least tolerable. He would have
shrieked at them to go away, had not the mere effort
of breathing and the slight movements involved been
exquisite pain. The zealot Levi, affected perhaps in
the same way, but reacting after the fashion of his
kind, shouted abuse, it sometimes seemed for minutes
together. The zealot Levi was another buzzing fly not
to be borne. If he suffered in his own world, need he
obtrude on that of Joseph?

It was intolerable not to move, yet worse to do so.
Weight must be shifted from crucified hands to crucified feet. Aching neck lolled or must be raised. Head
turned from side to side because it only was free to
move as it would. Wrestling with his pain, his
glazing eyes questing relief in heaven or earth, Joseph
glanced at the figure which hung on the cross by his
side. And the preacher looked at him.

Joseph knew at once that it was the healer, since the
vision in some sort was the same — the misting of his

own eyes, and the dazzle of light. In the shock of un-expected knowledge, he beheld the face of the preacher actually turned to him in great compassion.

Joseph moved his head away, seeking a new posi-tion. Yet though it was not easy to focus on any out-side thing, the thought remained with him that the preacher in his own agony had felt for another's.

There was such a gulf between that selflessness and the narrow confines of Joseph's particular world that he could hardly comprehend it. Nor was this a mo-ment for new revelations. Dimly, and as an idea to which he might pay attention when he had any to spare, he perceived that the face of the preacher was different from all other faces. The blindness in him which had made everyone else seem alike did not oper-ate here. But this was all his thought, the merest im-perceptible stirring of the surface of his mind. He was hardly conscious of it, so urgent was the fierce neces-sity of another movement.

The preacher, it seemed, had meanwhile turned his compassion on Levi. For the man burst out in a new tirade, this time directed against that figure in their midst over which Pilate as a supreme insult had writ-ten, "The King of the Jews." It was intolerable to be thus distracted from dying. But now Joseph actually felt it on behalf of the silent one by his side, as well as himself.

He made the terrible effort of taking breath and lift-ing his head. Sweat burst out on his forehead with fresh pain as he called to Levi, "Be silent in the name of God! If you and I are punished, is it not for our own sins? What has this man done?"

The preacher turned to him again, aware what speech had cost him. Then Joseph spoke to him out of his blindness, appealing as he might have done long ago, "Lord, remember *me* . . . when thou comest into thy kingdom." For no one in the world, save the preacher and himself, was real to him.

The preacher smiled and accepted him, never heeding whether he came seeing or still blind. "Tomorrow thou shalt be with me in paradise," he answered. With this promise, Joseph turned back into his own agony, holding to himself new thoughts which he might pursue . . . in paradise . . . when he had leisure.

SECTION II
A.D. 30 – A.D. 50

THE  DEATH OF AN EMPEROR

THE FIRST impression that Timothy had of his uncle's house was that of bareness. Not that it was not well-built of stone and standing in a good section — better, he thought, than his father's own in Alexandria, where the Jewish quarter was crowded into the Delta, so that the presence of the noisy, dirty commercial port was always with it. But his father Jason (Jeshu, as he must be called in Jerusalem) had decorated his walls Greek-style with bands of painting and his floors with colored mosaics. His hangings, his carpets, the couches on which they entertained their gentile customers were Persian work and glowing with the reds and blues which Babylonian merchants had introduced to all the civilized world. Here in contrast everything was plain — the walls mere whitewash, the floor stone flags well smoothed and set together, but bare of pattern. The carpet on which they sat was brown and white like the robes of his uncle and cousin. There was carving on the chest of the sacred scrolls, to be sure. The lamp was silver and burned a scented oil. The wine set out for him was delicately spiced. But amid these surroundings, Timothy himself glowed like a foreign thing, his linen garments white in the Egyptian fashion, yet gold-embroidered, the cloak which he had laid aside creating a splash of scarlet in the corner of the room. Uncomfortably, he was aware how his ear-rings, the chain about his neck, the ring on his finger, contrasted with the plain leather straps which bound the parchment of the sacred scrolls about his kinsmen's foreheads.

His first thought was, "Jason might have warned me." It was succeeded by slight indignation. Though Timothy did not wear the phylacteries himself, he was perfectly conscious of when this should be done; and he suspected that his uncle and cousin were trying to make him look awkward.

There was nothing in his uncle's manner to bear this out. Tobias was gracious, received the messages of his brother (Jeshu, Timothy must remember — not Jason), complimented the young man on having a look of his father, and inquired after every circumstance of his journey. His small, black eyes were watchful, how-ever. He had certainly noticed when Timothy touched the sacred scrolls at the doorposts, possibly suspect-ing from the slight clumsiness of the gesture that he was not in the habit of making it at home. When he suggested that his guest say the blessing, he had lis-tened to Timothy's Hebrew with critical approval and nodded slightly to himself. Fresh from his studies, the young man had welcomed a chance to show off and felt that he had acquitted himself well. But his cousin had frowned as though after all he spoke with an accent.

He was a formidable man, this cousin Seth, eight years older than Timothy himself and possessed of a presence which the younger man could never hope to rival. Short and clumsily built, he appeared to greater advantage at rest than in motion, seated than standing. But whatever he said or did was given dignity by the grandeur of a head whose hawklike profile was almost startlingly handsome. Seth had only to sit with his hands folded, as now, to look like Moses. He had only to let his dark glance rest on Timothy to make the young man blush with sudden discomfort.

"Did you hear any news?" his uncle was asking.

"News?" Timothy was nervous and did not for a moment comprehend the question, which was merely that asked of any traveler who might have picked up gossip in the ports through which he came. As enlightenment dawned, he felt more foolish than ever. "Oh, nothing," his face was scarlet now, "except the rumor there is abroad that the emperor is dying."

Seth leaned forward hastily. "Really dying?" But Timothy did not know or greatly care. Rome was very distant and her governors in the East were rarely changed. If they were so, one arrogant Roman was merely replaced by another. Timothy's father invariably grumbled; but he made money, and life went on as before.

"If one but knew who was the heir," his uncle mused.

"Why, Gaius, whom they nickname Caligula. Who other?"

"If Gaius is still alive," his cousin Seth pointed out darkly.

Even Timothy repressed a slight shudder. The last years of the old emperor had been so terrible that none could predict his murderous whims. A sudden suspicion — and there had been many such — could change the succession within a day, an hour. Yet how should this matter to the East, where trading prospered, great cities rose, and fortunes were founded? The Roman peace, unbroken since the great Augustus's time, encompassed all. "These problems are too political for me," Timothy shrugged. "In Alexandria, we Jews live unto ourselves, since affairs of government are all bound up with idol worship. In visiting the land of my fathers, I confess my thoughts are upon other subjects."

"It is a pity that my cousin arrives so late for the Temple," Seth agreed in his halting Greek. "Already the trumpet for evening sacrifice has blown. Timotheus," he was careful to emphasize the Greek name, "must be anxious to delay no longer in performing his duties."

This was definitely unfriendly. Timothy stiffened. It was true that his first visit to the Temple had been overdue since he was twelve years old. But to be reminded of the delay was a reflection on Jason himself, who had insisted that Timothy finish his education first. "Tomorrow will be time enough for the Temple," he said with a carelessness he by no means felt. "Or the next day. Since Jason," he made no attempt to use the Hebrew name, "chose I should wait, it does not become me to enter in haste now like a tardy schoolboy."

"It is written, 'I will go into thy house with burnt offerings. I will pay thee my vows.' "

Timothy glanced at his uncle, but Tobias sat impassive, apparently counting the gold threads in the border of Timothy's cloak across the room. It was borne in on the young man that his kinsmen were really angry because he had not come sooner. Yet surely his duty to the Temple was his own affair. It must be because of the girl.

"It is also written," he said, trying to make all right, " 'every daughter . . . shall be wife unto one of the family of the tribe of her father.' "

His uncle did stir at that, settling himself back more at his ease and seeming to smile. Possibly he had wondered if the girl was to be unclaimed. She must be fully sixteen, an awkward age to find a match, unless she were pretty.

"You may tell Hannah," Tobias beckoned to the servant, and he actually winked at his nephew in what seemed like an effort to be jolly, "that her husband is in haste to make her acquaintance."

"I drink to my bride," responded the young man

with a laugh. He drained his cup. Tobias lifted his;
but Seth, whose habits appeared abstemious, ignored
the toast.

"My sister is a pearl among the daughters of Israel,"
he remarked, his eyes surveying the youthful figure
and flushed face of Timothy, who was watching the
doorway in half-amusement, half-apprehension as he
waited to see who would be mother of his sons. "Too
good for you," Seth's expression added; but Timothy
interpreted it as merely meaning that Hannah was un-
attractive to the eye. He sighed inwardly, having had
hopes that she would be tolerable. But it did not matter, since it was his duty . . .

She was coming now, and both his kinsmen were
watching to see how she affected him. To his inner
fury, Timothy turned bright red and felt the beads of
sweat spring up across his forehead.

The girl parted the hanging and stood in the arch-
way, her eyes modestly cast down.

His first impression was a disappointment. "She is
so small!" His second, "She has dressed up for me, at
least." The little figure glowed with embroidery. The
dark hair, oiled and perfumed, rippled softly. The natural color of the face had been concealed by fine white
powder, the eyes lengthened and carefully shadowed,
their size and color obscured by her darkened lashes.
It was like looking at a doll, or at one of the images
which the Greeks carried round in their religious pro-
cessions.

Timothy stepped forward to take his bride by the

hand. It was warm and trembled inside his own. Beneath the powder, he could actually detect a flush on her cheeks, while her lips were parted to let breath in and out in panting motions. It dawned on Timothy that the girl was frightened.

In his careless, masculine way, it had not occurred to Timothy to wonder how Hannah liked her match. Marriage was a business to which young men must come, but one suitable maiden was as good as another. Possibly all husbands were not equally kind; but Timothy, who was young and popular and rich, had so much in his favor that it had never entered his head that she might not like him. With a shock of surprise, he now comprehended that a gentle maiden, cherished in her father's house, might dread the removal with a stranger to a strange land where she knew no one.

For a moment, he did not know what to say. If he had been holding a quivering bird in his hand, he would have stroked it. Under the watchful eyes of his kinsmen, such endearments were impossible. Collecting himself, he said to her very gently, in his halting Aramaic, "My little sisters have charged me to hasten home with their new playmate."

Timothy's sisters, who worshipped their magnificent brother from afar, had never stood him in better stead. Their very existence was reassuring. Timidly Hannah raised great brown eyes to his face and smiled for a heart-stopping moment. She let her glance fall again; but when he pressed her fingers, he thought he could detect a faint response.

Tobias came bustling forward; and Hannah, taking this as a signal to be gone, removed her fingers from Timothy's grasp and glided behind the curtain.

"Well, well," cried Tobias with that forced jollity which Timothy already disliked. "Does she please, eh? Does she please?" Seth, still looking like the prophet Moses, said nothing.

"She is a flower," said Timothy fervently, "a white lily."

"No, no!" Tobias laughed. "She is as brown as you or I, but white is the fashion." Clearly, however, the compliment pleased him, and he would repeat it.

"White or brown," said Timothy, "she is a rare flower." He was horrified to think how long and carelessly he had put off coming to claim her and how easily his uncle might have lost patience. Seth, it was obvious, had not forgiven him yet, so that it was politic to let his eagerness show. No hint of discord must mar his understanding with these relations.

"Why, then, we need not delay," cried his uncle, clapping him on the shoulder. "A rare flower, eh? No doubt, the sooner the better!"

"Timotheus," said Seth, unstirring from his place, "will wish to perform his sacrifice at the Temple."

"No doubt, no doubt." The sudden change in Tobias's expression was a revelation of the real master of the house. "First things first. Perhaps also Timothy will listen to the wisdom of the rabbis. Seth," he added, turning to his nephew with pride, "is a disciple of Rabbi Eleazar . . . of the school of Shammai."

The rabbi's name was one to conjure with in Israel. Timothy was impressed, but the condescension with which his uncle had explained that Eleazar belonged to the great conservative school was an affront. Did they think him as ignorant as that? "I, too, have studied our Law," he said, forcing himself to appear calm. "Under Alexander."

"Alexander? Oh, the Egyptian! I fear you will find our rabbis far beyond you."

From the unconcern of Seth's tone, it was clear that he had no intention of being rude. He really did think that the vast learning and wide culture of Alexander counted for nothing beside the rabbinical studies of Eleazar. Since even Alexander agreed that the Law was the fount of all wisdom, possibly Timothy ought not to have resented his cousin's arrogance. He had, however, been devoted to his master, who had shown him how the philosophy of the Greeks was only a fashion of seeking to comprehend the one true God. Too young to perceive that a defence of higher culture would do him no good with Seth, he rushed in angrily.

"What do you know about Alexander's learning? Have you read Plato?"

"A pagan? I should hope not!"

"Did Moses forbid the study of Greek? Or if pagans admit their own ignorance, must we despise their search for God? My saintly master was wont to quote a Greek epitaph which he had once read. 'I die against my will; whither I go, I know not.' It reduced him, he said, to tears of pity."

He stopped, dismayed. His cousin had said nothing, merely raising his eyebrows to look across at Tobias, who shook his head.

"I am a Hebrew of the Hebrews, even as you are," Timothy insisted.

"And a looker-on at the games of the Greeks, or do I wrong you?"

"Does Moses forbid it?"

"A frequenter of their impious theaters?"

"I still keep the Law."

"And to this half-pagan you give your daughter?"

Tobias, addressed point-blank, shrugged sulkily. "He is my brother's son; and Jeshu's influence, even in Rome, is great."

The apology in his tone brought home to Timothy how every compromise with the culture of the Greeks was considered loathesome. Here in Jerusalem, where the fire of Judaism burned with steady flame, a man was either a pious Jew or a Romanizer, either a patriot or the servant of the oppressor. No learning existed at all, save the Law of the Lord. To Timothy, born and brought up in one of the greatest centers of Greek culture in the world, it was as natural to study the Greeks as his own faith. Nor did he consider his zeal for the Holy One affected thereby. He tried to say so.

"I keep the Law of the Holy One, blessed be He. Can you do more? I come to the Temple . . ."

"After these many years!"

Timothy felt himself growing red. To argue with his cousin was like beating at a great wall, massive, dignified, and quite impervious to kicks or blows. He could only hurt himself. With a violent effort he kept control of his temper and, turning to his uncle, pleaded fatigue. The exertions of his journey had been great. If they would excuse him . . .

"Of course, of course!" Tobias, evidently eager to smooth over ill-feeling, took the conversation into his own hands. He sent for Timothy's servant, fussed over his comfort, apologized for deficiencies of the house, while constantly stealing side-glances at his son as though he were hoping to receive a sign of approval. If so, he did not get it. Seth frowned magnificently, withdrawing into dignified silence only broken by a shocked reminder when poor Timothy plunged heedlessly through the door without making the gesture of touching his hand to the sacred scrolls.

It was notable that since Seth's protest, nothing more had been said about Hannah. Timothy, retiring to think things over, perceived that the marriage which he had long taken for granted was by no means as certain a thing as he had supposed. Unaccustomed to being denied what he wished, he immediately made up his mind that Hannah was the wife he would have. Their brief meeting had been hardly sufficient for falling in love; but she had pleased him, and his spoiled nature did the rest. Besides, he was conscious of desiring a victory over his cousin Seth.

His first duty on the days succeeding was to religion. Timothy's conduct, following a private resolution, was exemplary. He performed all his ritual duties, gave to the Temple a voluntary gift of such size that even Seth nodded approval, and listened manfully to learned rabbis disputing in a language he could hardly follow. By presenting a letter to the leaders of the Greek-speaking synagogue, he escaped the attention of his cousin for part of the Sabbath, using the respite chiefly to strengthen his resolution. He made no effort to see Tobias alone; but as soon as he did so, he pressed on him the gift which the bridegroom must give to the bride's father.

This consisted of but a single object, the seal ring which Timothy had worn for safety's sake on his own finger. It was, however, one of the greatest treasures of his father's stock, an emerald with a microscopic device incredibly carved by a great artist. The jewel had been owned by Herod Agrippa, an intimate of the Emperor's dead son and of his present heir Gaius. Agrippa had borrowed money of the merchants in Egypt in order to go to Rome and recoup his fortunes. Timothy mentioned the history of the gem in an offhand way. The Herods might be considered half-Jews, but they were royal. It was something to have the goodwill of an imperial favorite, no matter who he might be. Tobias frowned at the ring, turning it over in his hands and probably reflecting that he could not get a comparable price for his daughter in all Jerusalem. Indeed, the value of the present exceeded her dowry, Timothy suspected. Tobias was not conspicuously rich, and Seth was above money-getting.

"Well, well," Tobias concluded, "it is a great gift."

He had looked for a minute as though he were intending to hand it back. Now, sighing heavily, he unlocked his chest to lay it inside.

"Let me see my bride again," urged Timothy, carefully waiting until the chest was closed and the key put away. "Since she must travel so far from her home, she will be eager to learn what sort of place she is to live in."

It was perfectly clear that in accepting Timothy's ring, Tobias had already gone further along the road of consent than he really wished. Having done so, however, he could hardly refuse to send for Hannah. She came, as Timothy was glad to see, in what must be her everyday garments with no powder on her delicate olive complexion and no perfume in her hair. Clearly she had not expected to see Timothy with her father. She flushed, looking timidly at them as though she feared dismissal. Perhaps they had told her there was to be no match after all. If so, there was not time for explanations. Timothy took her by the hand, made her sit beside him, and searched his memory for anecdotes of his father, mother, and sisters. His conversation could hardly have been termed a courtship, but it served to reestablish him in the girl's own eyes as her future master. Pressing her hand as he had done before, he let her tell him by that tiny answering pressure that she liked the notion. Encouraged, he spun out his talk as far as his Aramaic would permit. Characteristically, no one had thought it worthwhile to teach Hannah Greek, though it was known that Tim-

othy's mother, a Jewess from Alexandria, spoke no
other language.

Half an hour passed pleasantly. In answer to a question, Hannah murmured a soft reply, after referring to
her father's face in case of disapproval. Tobias did not
meet her gaze. He had a weakness for his daughter and
perceived she liked the young man. He was fond of
his brother, too, and wished to keep his word about
the marriage. Matters of policy made a connection between the Pharisees and Herod Agrippa to be desired.
In these uncertain times everybody who could establish
a claim on the new heir must hasten to do so. The government of Judaea, since the recall of Pontius Pilate
last year, was awaiting imperial settlement. In fact,
Timothy was a pawn in a larger game. Notwithstanding, Tobias knew he had gone too fast in accepting the
bridegroom's gift and permitting this intimate conversation. For one thing, he felt doubtful about poor
Timothy himself, though for the last days his zeal had
been encouraging. But his upbringing had been de-
plorable. Tobias was accustomed to being ruled by
Seth and knew that disapproval from his son would
weigh heavily on him.

Captivated by the task of wooing Hannah, Timothy
himself gave no thought to larger issues. What he had
done so far to win his bride had been by calculation.
By now, however, he found himself carried away.
Hannah, pretty and gentle, responsive yet hard to get,
combined in her person the very qualities which most
enticed him. Timothy, who had known no young girls

except his sisters, had never been in love before and found it agreeable. Accordingly, he watched entranced while the delicate color came and went on Hannah's face, smiled when she smiled, and thought himself a fine fellow because the sweetest girl in the world hung on his lips.

He was sent for by his uncle a few hours later and found him with Seth. Tobias looked angry.

"How dare you bring an uncircumcised man into my household?"

There was a blank silence. Timothy's servant was, to be sure, a Greek. It was the practice among the stricter Israelites to give their servants the choice of being circumcised or resold. But in Egypt these things were not done. As long as a slave abstained from idol worship and from eating unclean food, he was not troubled by an initiation rite which some of them dreaded.

"How can I give my daughter's hand to such a man?"

Timothy found himself growing angry. He knew perfectly well his uncle's protest was merely an excuse to slip out of a bargain which Seth did not approve of. "It is now too late for second thoughts," he said very stiffly. "The matter is settled."

"My father is not to be bought," put in Seth. "Take back your ring."

The jewel was in Tobias's hand, but Timothy ignored it.

"The arrangement was between your father and myself," he said hotly to his cousin. "It is a matter in which you have no voice."

"And you offer as a bribe the very seal ring of that half-Jew, that Romanized Herod, that Agrippa whom your connections have sent adventuring to Rome! Such a present disgraces giver and receiver alike. Take it back!"

"The ring was sold to my father," Timothy said defiantly. "It did belong to Agrippa once, and for that reason Jason sent it. When the old emperor dies, my father says Agrippa will rule the Jews like his grandfather, Herod the Great. Agrippa is not unmindful of his friends, or of his enemies either."

"The emperor," Seth said ominously, "is not dead, I hear. Agrippa is in prison."

So the old madman's suspicions had caught up with Agrippa! For a moment, the fate of a prince he had known and admired brought home to Timothy the shifting ground on which they all stood. Had not his father been one of Agrippa's backers? Rome, however, was another world. Those who went there took their lives in their hands. Political rumblings, like distant thunder in the air, meant little. Storms passed by on one side or the other. Meanwhile, he and Hannah had their own future to settle.

"If the ring is worth nothing in influence," he said hardily, "it is also worth money. Few bridegrooms can give such a jewel."

"There are values," Seth told him unmoved, "far

greater than influence or money. Go offer your treasure for a girl who can be bought, not for my sister."

"It is your sister I will have," retorted Timothy, and
from this position nothing would budge him. Desperately clinging to his position as guest, he lived with
his uncle and cousin in an angry silence, never seeing
the slightest sign that either was relenting. For Tobias
was fearful of the connection now that Agrippa was
almost certainly dead, while Seth for his part was im-
movable in his dislike of Timothy's habits. Hannah,
whose opinion no one asked, did weep for Timothy, as
he ascertained through the servants. She, however,
must do what she was told. Still, Timothy wondered
if the difficulties of disposing of a grown girl elsewhere had occurred to Seth. Surely he would not
doom her to die unmarried out of spite! Unconscious
of any larger issue, Timothy put Seth's opposition
down to pettiness. It even occurred to him that because Tobias was not rich, his cousin was jealous.

He took his problem in the end to a connection of
his mother's, a Grecianized Jew who had long ago settled in Jerusalem, partly from piety, but partly from
a compulsion to be at the center of things. Philip,
though not influential himself, had made it his life work
to know those who were. Listening to Timothy with a
kindly but disillusioned eye, he pursed his lips.

"One girl is as good as another. Why trouble with
this one?"

Timothy went bright red. "My father wishes it."

"Very dutiful, to be sure! But your uncle does not."

"Tobias is willing," Timothy persisted. "It is my cousin who makes trouble, and for no reason. I am as good an Israelite as he."

Out of long experience, Philip shook his head. "No one is ever as good in the eyes of the Holy One, blessed be He, as are the Pharisees. Their life is given to the Law. While we indulge ourselves in things not expressly forbidden, they do only that which has been commanded. There is a difference which is visible here, though in Alexandria one may not perceive it."

"Are such distinctions for women? Or must every husband be a rabbi?"

"I say to you again, there are other girls."

"This is the only one for me," confessed Timothy, shamefaced.

Philip raised his eyebrows skeptically. "You are young, Timothy, and must have what you think you want. No issues are as simple as that in Jerusalem. The emperor is dying."

"Why should I care for that?" asked Timothy, surprised. "All I want is the girl."

"If she is married elsewhere, you will have to forget her."

Timothy started. No hint of an alternative match for Hannah had reached his ears. The girl's age and dowry were both against it. If he had comprehended that there had been any such plan, he might have retired from a hopeless contest while he could yield gracefully. By now, he was too deeply in love. He gave Philip an angry, interrogative glance and set his teeth.

Philip did not meet his gaze. "Rabbi Eleazar," he said, regarding his own fingers, "has recently lost a wife. It would be an honor for your cousin Seth to be connected with his rabbi."

"Rabbi Eleazar! That graybeard!" Timothy choked with horror. "He must be forty years Hannah's elder."

"It would be a proud match for a daughter of Israel."

"But little Hannah . . ." Tears actually started to Timothy's eyes. She would feel it her duty, a privilege even. Little Hannah! "What right has Eleazar to steal my bride?"

"We-ell, if a promise was given you . . ." Philip considered. "How can you prove it?"

"I'll not need proof. I'll make a mockery of old Eleazar desiring a young bride. I'll mingle with his students in the Temple, and I'll ask him in front of them all . . ."

"You'll not get away with a whole skin," Philip said.

Despairingly, Timothy knew he was right. The followers of the rabbinical schools were even ready to descend to blows over ritual questions. How much more so if anyone made a public mockery of their rabbi. Nor would Timothy profit from creating such a scandal. His uncle and cousin would be sure to refuse him the girl, even if the rabbi judged it prudent to renounce her. Everyone would be angry and Hannah still lost to him. It would not do.

"The matter is not decided yet," said Philip consolingly. "Rabbi Eleazar is not of an age to be precipitate, and he still mourns his wife. But the thing has been talked of."

"What shall I do?" cried Timothy, wrung to the heart for the first time in his young and careless life. "What shall I do?"

"You had better leave things in my hands," Philip told him, "though I cannot tell how they will turn out. It would still be wisest for you to go back to your father and forget this girl."

"That at least I cannot do," retorted Timothy, triumphant. "My father has written that he wishes me to remain here for the present."

Disconcertingly, Philip nodded, saying that Jason was a far-seeing man. If the emperor were to die without replacing Flaccus as governor of Egypt, there would be trouble between the Greeks and Jews there. Was there as much racial hatred in Alexandria as ever, did Timothy suppose?

On such a subject, Timothy had no views. He had grown up with the ill-feeling which existed and had deplored it because the gymnasiums of the Greeks were closed to him. But he had never actually seen any bloodshed. Besides, his generous nature bore no malice and suspected none. "Just as usual," he answered Philip indifferently. "There are frequently quarrels among the poorer sort at the edge of the Quarter where Greeks and Jews intermingle. But we keep ourselves to ourselves for the most part."

"Hm! Well, these are dangerous times with the old emperor dying and too little known about the new one. Your father is right to take his precautions. But you young men think your affairs of love are all-important."

This was just what Timothy did think. That violent upheavals could be caused by a death in Rome seemed too improbable to be considered. Older people liked to shake heads and look knowing while delivering themselves of some gloomy prophecy. Timothy had noticed that when they proved wrong, they forgot what they had said; while if they were right, they put on airs about it. As for Philip's advice to leave things to him, he never considered it for a moment. For one thing, his own position in his uncle's house was becoming unbearable.

The fact was, Timothy felt bored. He had already been on his best behavior far too long. The Roman governor of Syria was in the town, making halfhearted preparations for a campaign which the old emperor had ordered, but the new one might not care for. In the course of putting things off, he had entertained himself and his friends by celebrating games in the stadium built by Herod. They had been a very good show, and Timothy would have liked to have gone. The brothers and sons of the High Priest had attended, he knew, though the Priest himself had not ventured to do so. Among the young men of the fashionable set, Timothy might have had the sort of good time that he was used to. He even had introductions with him, which he had abstained from presenting. Instead, he had haunted the Temple, tried to look pious and to make a good impression on the rabbis. Timothy was in earnest about his religion, but he was not used to so much of it at once. Nor had all his virtue gained him a sight of Hannah, who was strictly confined to the women's quarters of the house.

It was at this stage that he received an invitation to dine at the High Priest's. Since the sacred office was openly bought from the Roman governor, it followed that only the wealthy and pro-Roman obtained it. Strict Pharisees like Seth despised the High Priest almost as much as they respected his office. It was therefore a sign of open revolt to dine at his table. Announcing it to his uncle and cousin, Timothy perceived at once that they were angry. "He is a connection, though a distant one, of my mother's," he told them blandly, quite conscious that they did not like any talk of his mother, to whose influence they attributed his foreign education.

There was nothing more to be said; and Timothy went, returning very late and in a manner which sadly upset the routine of the household. But the celebration had not entirely been a jolly one. News had been imparted to the High Priest by his Roman friends which had lent a certain sobriety to the occasion. Timothy with an air of self-satisfaction passed it on to his kinsmen.

"Gaius Caligula, who was the emperor's heir, is certainly dead."

Since he did not greatly care himself, he was astonished to see how much his kinsmen did so. Tobias went quite pale, while even Seth deserted his habitual silence to inquire sharply, "Who said that?"

"The High Priest, who had it from the Romans," Timothy said. "It seems the doctors gave the old emperor up for dead. Everybody hurried to congratulate Gaius at once. But while he was receiving the throng, Tiberius woke up and called for wine."

There was a shocked silence. Old Tiberius had killed many men for lesser offenses. The fate of Gaius, and indeed of those who were with him, was decided.

"The fool!" cried Seth suddenly in quivering anger. "The stupid fool! They would have smothered the old man in his own bedclothes if Gaius had dared to give the word. They must have done so for the sake of their own lives. Who knows what the emperor's grandson, who is but a child, will be like, or who will rule him? Gaius at least . . ."

"Will you not hold your tongue?" Tobias interrupted. "Have you no prudence?"

There was a silence. Timothy with the eyes of the other two upon him went first red, then white. His cousin's coldblooded proposal to smother a dying old man had really shocked him. But the evident distrust of his uncle was even worse. It dawned on Timothy for the first time that his kinsmen's treatment of him was not entirely a personal affair. He, Timothy, born in the old emperor's reign, had not comprehended what a change of rulers involved. Why the whole world was holding its breath, and everybody was looking at everyone else, while fearful questions trembled unspoken. What, for instance, would happen to the friends of Gaius's friends when they came under scrutiny of his successful rival? Timothy's father was known to have backed Herod Agrippa with money. Was it for this reason that Jason had forbidden his son to return to Egypt?

The palms of Timothy's hands were wet, but he looked at his uncle straight in the eyes and said, "You had better give back Agrippa's ring. It may be dangerous to you. No doubt my father will provide a costlier gift."

Tobias fumbled with his chest in silence. Timothy took the ring out of his hand and put it on, feeling as though it were a badge which marked him for danger. With what dignity he could muster, he got up, turned his back on his kinsmen, and walked out, once more forgetting to touch the sacred scrolls upon the door-post. This time, however, not even his cousin Seth called him back to do so.

Timothy needed time to think. That he had lost Hannah was an obvious fact which hardly seemed to concern him. He could not have taken her for his wife if his father or he himself were to be in trouble. More immediate was the problem of whether he should go back to Egypt in defiance of Jason. A caution new to him bade him think this over. Such a question could not be decided in the close confines of his uncle's house or in the crowded streets. Instinctively, he turned his steps to the Temple. Timothy was not accustomed to taking his problems before the God of his fathers, since in general he never had any. His religion was ritual exactly performed and duty done. Today, however, he felt no hesitation. In the Court of Israel a man might offer his private prayers without any comment. It was not early in the day because his own arising had been exceedingly late. The solemn ritual of the evening sacrifice would calm his mind.

He did feel fortified, and the decision which he came to had sense. He could not help his father, but in case of trouble he might perhaps assist his mother and sisters. Timothy might be used to a good time, but he was not really selfish. When forced to consider serious things, he did not attempt to gloss them over. He perceived he was dealing with problems which he did not himself understand and he must have advice. He would go to Philip, admit his ignorance, and ask what he ought to do. He did not particularly care to encounter Philip's amused contempt, now knowing what a fool he must have seemed at their earlier encounter; but he was not going to let such feelings make a difference. The question before him was how he might best be of use, and not how he felt. As for Hannah, he must not think of her. She would be better without him. Soberly, but quite determined on his course, Timothy went to Philip's house.

It had not occurred to him that Philip would be at dinner and that there might be difficulty in seeing him without an appointment. Philip sent out word that he was talking business, but that if Timothy liked to wait, the servants would look after him.

Timothy hesitated. There was a great deal of bustle, and he understood that his presence was unwelcome. All the same, he was not willing to return to his uncle without having made up his mind. Uncertainly, he was refusing perfunctory offers of refreshment from a harried steward when somebody clapped him on the shoulder.

"Why, here he is! We might have known it. When anything happens, we all run to Philip!"

Timothy, starting uncomfortably, turned round on a latecoming guest who seemed by his manner to have dined quite well already. The face was only faintly familiar, and it gave him no pleasure to have it pressed close against his own, while its owner said, breathing heavily, "My cousin was looking for you half the day. Where have you been?"

"In the Temple," said Timothy shortly, trying to place him.

"Ho-ho!" He doubled up, laughing. "In the Temple! And my cousin looked everywhere else. I always tell him he is too politically minded for his office."

Timothy, who by now vaguely remembered this loudmouthed person at the jolly dinner which he had attended the previous night, extracted himself from the other's embrace and said cautiously, "I cannot imagine what your cousin should desire to see me about."

His companion winked knowingly. "He has a use for everybody. He is politically minded, as I told you. The truth is, all the Herodians in Jerusalem hold by Antipas, who is on the worst of terms with his nephew Agrippa. Yet the High Priest has more to gain from Agrippa than most as things now stand. Can you wonder that he gives thought to how he may approach him?"

"Approach Agrippa? The High Priest?" Timothy was quite at sea.

The red-faced man put an arm on his shoulder again and swayed closer to breathe into his ear. "It is rumored that the government of the whole land is to be reconsidered by the new emperor. Now if Agrippa . . ."

"The new emperor?" Timothy's evident confusion produced another burst of laughter.

"Ho-ho, not heard the news! At his prayers in the Temple all day. In the Temple! My cousin will laugh!"

"I have heard," said Timothy, flushing with annoyance, "how Agrippa was thrown into prison and probably dead, while Gaius Caligula . . ."

"Ah, that's all past and gone. Gaius took Agrippa out of prison the moment the old man died. He decorated him with a gold chain in memory of his fetters, and he has made him tetrarch of Perea beyond Jor-

dan. Agrippa is now all-powerful in Rome, and everybody . . ."

"But we were told last night," protested Timothy,
"how Gaius Caligula . . ."

"Is emperor!" interrupted the other. He leaned
against Timothy's ear again and actually lowered his
voice. "Last night's rumor . . . a tale that got abroad
nobody knows how . . . is to be forgotten. Tiberius
. . . well, he died."

Timothy gave an involuntary shudder. Had Gaius,
entrapped by the old man's sudden revival, resorted to
murder? If he, Timothy, had stood in Gaius's shoes,
what would he have done? As it was, the ring on his
finger might, indeed now must, buy him Hannah. It
could so easily have bought imprisonment, ruin, or
death, had the old emperor lived but another week. It
was a sobering reflection.

"Hey!" His companion shook him. "I say, had you
not best go to my cousin? You need not stand on ceremony with him now, you know. You have become
important!"

"Behold the bridegroom!" Philip himself was standing on the threshold, smiling at him with his characteristically sardonic air. "I have slipped away from my
guests to please your impatience. As it happens, your
little matter is all arranged — though I must confess
to you that there are more important things on my
mind at present."

Timothy went scarlet. It appeared as though in
his selfishness he had rushed to Philip as soon as Agrippa

was known to be the new favorite. Philip was angry at having been asked to bother with his wedding at a time of public crisis. Unable to explain, Timothy felt his dignity hopelessly lost as he made his excuses. "I will not trouble you with my thanks for the present, since you are busy."

Philip raised critical eyebrows. "You might have thought of that before. But you are young."

"You must remember me to Jason, your father," insisted the cousin of the High Priest.

Timothy, still ignorant of the man's name, was grateful for the interruption. "I will certainly do so."

"This young man has other things in mind," said Philip unmercifully. "He is to be married, which is in his own eyes more important than grave political business."

"Ho-ho-ho!" The High Priest's cousin roared again. "Young girls are all the same, but young men do not think so."

"They do not think at all," retorted Philip.

Timothy felt himself growing angry. He had told himself that he did not need to justify his ways to Philip, but this was unfair. Young men of Timothy's age and set were encouraged by their fathers to have a good time. He had pursued his studies, had not ever been wildly extravagant, considering his father's wealth, had kept the religion of his fathers — had, in fact, done all that had been asked of him. Why should he be supposed to know about matters which had been kept from his attention?

"Young men," said Timothy, letting his indignation show, "are not brought up to think. It is the fault of their elders." But this sounded too like a criticism of his father, and he could not indulge in that. "Doubtless," he added, "the times are such that even their elders are at a loss to know their own opinions."

"Can it be that I did you injustice, Timothy?" inquired Philip lightly. But he was smiling.

THE ✿ ✿ ✿
BEES ✿ OF ✿
CAPERNAUM

IT HAPPENED as Nathaniel was putting on his Sabbath
clothes. This was not, as might be imagined, at dawn
or even near it. Nathaniel was a shoemaker by trade
and no great student of the Scriptures. He was, moreover, a fat man and in small things self-indulgent. It
had come to be understood that Sabbath morning was
devoted by him to meditation. This he usually did in
bed, his mind wandering vaguely between the affairs
of the Lord and his own. Since the latter were prosperous enough for his modest ambitions, Nathaniel rose
refreshed in body and mind on Sabbath mornings.
Ahead of him lay the climax of his week, the walk to
synagogue, the honorable place amid his fellows, the
pleasant after-gossips with mind at leisure, duty done,
and the long, quiet afternoon ahead. He would spend
siesta-time in the shade of his own little yard, back
propped against his olive tree, hands clasped on his
stomach. He would count abstractedly the number of
his ripening figs or watch his bees, of which he had
three pipes of good baked clay stopped carefully at
either end with mud. Their buzzing would soothe him
into falling asleep in a dream of figs and honey. There-

after, he would saunter down the street to watch with
his cronies while the sun went down in the sky and the
last golden hour of the Sabbath faded to its closing.

All these delights lay ahead of Nathaniel as with
complacent little gestures he patted his garments into
shape, squared his shoulders, passed a careful comb
through his beard, and glanced indulgently at the
portly swelling underneath his girdle. Presently he
picked up his shoes, bestowing on them a professional
nod of appreciation. Good leather and, though he said
it himself, good workmanship. Their second year of
Sabbath wear and very nearly as strong as ever. Some
shoemakers were content with shoddy work when it
came to sandals for which they would not be paid.
Nathaniel, and he thanked God for it, shod his family
as well as anybody else. His poor old mother was bed-
ridden by now, and his daughter Tabitha who waited
on her could not stir far from the house. Their shoes,
however, were as well-stitched as his own. Nathaniel
was a kindly master to his household, and it would have
distressed him to think that his women lacked befitting
garments.

He had stooped to put the shoes on, conceding a
grunt to the effort of bending, when Tabitha's voice
reached his ears from the yard below.

"Father! Oh, Father! Come quick! The bees are
swarming!"

It was a cry he had heard before, since bees can
swarm with little warning. So far, however, by the
blessing of the Holy One, Nathaniel's had respected

the Sabbath. As he stumbled down the outside stair with one shoe still in his hand, he was conscious of indignation. He had not deserved this. But it never entered his head to let the bees go. It stood to reason that, Sabbath or no Sabbath, he could not afford to.

He arrived in the yard as the bees were leaving it. One moment he was enveloped in buzzing. The next, he was clear; and the train of bees was sailing off. Essential that he discover where they alighted. People were so dishonest! And even on the Sabbath, it was not exactly work to *follow* one's bees.

Nathaniel panted down the street, his Sabbath clothes flapping between his legs, his arms working, his sandaled foot a mere impediment in the soft dust of the road. A couple of the dogs, who were always waiting about for garbage, saw a possible profit in his haste and ran barking at his heels. People popped heads out of their houses, all agog at the interruption of Sabbath quiet. One or two ironically cheered Nathaniel on.

The bees were outstripping Nathaniel, and presently they vanished. He drew up, panting. Never would he live this Sabbath down!

"Which way?"

People pointed eagerly in all directions. Nathaniel plunged on. Somebody shouted, "In there!" He darted through the doorway of a fenced yard and halted, puffing. In front of him, depending from the branch of a big olive, was the brown, shimmering mass of swarming bees.

"My cousin Nathaniel on a Sabbath visit!"

Nathaniel bounced round indignantly to face the speaker. Nothing that had happened was more rasping to his temper than that the bees should have alighted in the yard of his cousin Joazar, a man at whom respectable people like himself pursed up their lips.

There was little wrong with Joazar on the surface. He went to synagogue and kept the Sabbath. His profession, which was that of publican or tax-collector's agent, was against him. It was recognized, however, that he had inherited this from his father, who had collected customs duties between what had been till lately the borders of Herod Philip and Herod Antipas. This was not as bad as collecting for the Romans, and fairly recently the taxes had become almost excusable. The Emperor had lately granted Galilee, Perea, and even Judaea as well to Herod Agrippa, with the title of king. Agrippa, who was the first king of the Jews since the great Herod nearly fifty years before, proclaimed himself zealous for the Lord. There were those who said he was just another Herod; but many were well-disposed, for his rule was as yet new. His taxes were not at present a burning grievance. Joazar's dubious profession weighed only slightly against him, except of course with the very strictest. And a good many people were glad to deal with an understanding fellow who knew when to look the other way.

The trouble with Joazar was much more subtle. He was not a serious man. One could hear him laughing and joking with gentiles who brought goods into market and one could try to excuse him, since this was his business. But Joazar laughed at other times, as for instance when the president of the synagogue had handed the scrolls in person to a visiting rabbi and, being near of sight, had very nearly dropped them. Both men had bent over and saved the situation at the price of knocking together their venerable heads with a loud click. Joazar had been profuse with apologies, had said he was not thinking. But he had laughed.

He laughed now, too; and Nathaniel lost his temper. "Those bees are mine," he said, "and I've a right to take them. Plenty of people saw them come in, so don't try any tricks."

Joazar stiffened at his tone. "Did I deny that they were yours?"

"You can't," snapped Nathaniel, before whose heated vision the bees and the branch and his cousin Joazar swam in a fog which was thickened by sheer fury. Subconsciously his anger was directed more at the Holy One Himself than at Joazar. Was it necessary for bees to swarm on Sabbath mornings when other occasions would have suited them equally well? Did they have to drag a respectable man down the public street? His injured innocence, inflamed by Joazar's very presence, had brought him to a pitch of unreason which was foreign to his normal disposition.

"Are you going to tell me," asked Joazar mockingly, "that you want to take those bees and actually *carry* them down the street, and on the SABBATH!"

"You don't think I'll leave them with you!" retorted Nathaniel. His conscience was clear enough. There were special emergencies on which work had to be performed, come when they would. It was not the work, but the publicity which would create a scandal. Some purists always took a strict view, forgetting that a tradesman dare omit nothing which might supplement his meager profits. If the bees had settled in any yard but Joazar's, Nathaniel would have left them with the owner for a day or two, repaying the favor with a gift of honey at the end of the season. The work involved in settling them into a home could then have been kept private.

"Have it your own way," said Joazar with increasing rudeness. "That is, if the bees are actually yours. I have only your word for it."

"Don't you dare lay claim to them!" cried Nathaniel, beside himself with manifold frustrations. He raised his fist to brandish it at Joazar and discovered that the sandal was still in it.

"They are in my yard," insisted Joazar, who for all his flippant ways had a temper which was well known to be quick. "Too bad I cannot stay out of synagogue to take them!"

This reminded Nathaniel that he could not, even for the bees, neglect attendance at synagogue. After that frantic progress up the street, no excuse would serve him. But Joazar might sneak back home, pretending illness. "I'll escort you to synagogue myself," he vowed, "and make sure you enter."

"Then you had better tidy your person," said Joazar unkindly. "It is not my custom to go out on the Sabbath with my headgear awry or with dust on my feet and sweat on my forehead. Nor do I carry my shoes in my hand. In fact, if you will excuse me . . ."

He vanished indoors, presumably in quest of his sandals, leaving Nathaniel to brush himself clean as well as he could in the dusty yard. In front of him the great brown ball of bees hung, tantalizing, just out of reach. In order to take them, he would have to get a ladder and a basket and an assistant. After synagogue, they might not still be there. At least, however, he would see that Joazar did not get them! Not one step would he stir, not a step without the fellow. Nathaniel planted himself across the gateway to wait for his cousin.

Joazar took his time. Nathaniel was almost ready to go into the house and drag him out. What, however, if he were to be stretched out on his bed, pretending a sudden bout of sickness? Hesitating, Nathaniel looked up at the bees and almost wished they would fly off out of reach. But they showed no signs of stirring.

By the time he was thoroughly uneasy, Joazar appeared, fresh and shining. He was humming a little to himself as he brushed past Nathaniel without appearing to notice that he was there. Plodding angrily at his heels, Nathaniel followed.

It was not easy to keep track of Joazar, because he walked quite fast, while poor Nathaniel had to run the gantlet of ironical queries. Luckily the villain was tall, and his bobbing headgear could be followed far down the street amid the more staid movements of more respectable men. So many people put themselves in Nathaniel's way that he was not able to keep that head continuously in sight. Eventually, a hundred yards from the synagogue, he lost it. Something appeared to snap inside him, and the impatient yet tolerable politeness with which he had fended off the humor of his neighbors abruptly vanished. Pushing angrily through the crowd, red-faced and careless of shaken heads behind him, he thrust forward into the dim, cool synagogue, where he peered around for his cousin.

Joazar, distinguishable still by his long back, was sitting quietly toward the rear in the society of others whose social standing was equally dubious. He had clearly come straight in without the slightest effort to slip away home. Nothing could be more unsuspicious than his conduct, save that he deliberately looked around the hall, caught the eye of his cousin, and winked.

It was such a knowing, such a triumphant wink that Nathaniel halted, almost willing to try and push himself out again through the door. Someone behind him prodded him, and he emitted an audible groan which earned him a look of surprise from one or two near enough to hear it over the hubbub. There was really no help for him. He had to go forward, lower himself to his place amid his fellows, and try and persuade himself that the expression of triumph on his cousin's face meant simply nothing.

Midway through the rabbi's exposition, enlightenment came to him. The boy! He knew there was one, maybe two. He had dismissed them in his mind as being too small to take the bees or even — and he had considered the point — assist their mother. But not too small to take messages! And Joazar knew gentiles who did not keep the Sabbath. Of course he did because of his profession! He did them favors, no doubt, as he did Jews. There was no knowing what a man like Joazar might not do for gentiles. He would not even care if their polluted hands had touched the bees. His bees! And stolen on the Sabbath! Nathaniel emitted another groan which he was forced to convert into the appearance of a terrible pain in his stomach. The rabbi had actually paused and was looking at him, as indeed was everybody else. Nathaniel rocked back and forth with a silent grimace which represented a real, though spiritual anguish. He had resigned himself, or thought he had, to the bees flying off; but that while he sat here . . . Sweat had started out on his forehead again, while his neighbors whispered irreverently and the rabbi raised his voice with a frown in their direction.

It was almost intolerable to wait. When synagogue was over, Nathaniel pushed his way through the gossiping crowds and actually trotted, though he could not quite bring himself to run. When he arrived, the branch on the olive tree was empty, as he had known it would be. The bees had gone!

"They must have flown away," said Joazar, shrugging and spreading his hands with an air of innocence.

But he grinned as he said the words, and Nathaniel did not believe him.

He was older than Joazar and smaller and fatter. It was useless to come to blows with him, and it was the Sabbath. Nathaniel, moreover, rather thought he was in deep enough trouble already. There was nothing for it but to go away, tail between legs, to the tune of mocking laughter.

This in itself was bad enough, but there was worse to follow. He had earned a certain notoriety, and these were peculiar times. Dark-visaged fanatics spread through the land. Gloomy heads were shaken over the backslidings of Israel. Rich people very often went their own way, a cause for fresh scandal. Little trades-men like Nathaniel, puzzled by strange prophecies, held up to rigid standards, ignorant, yet anxious to please, were at the mercy of popular opinions. Na-thaniel's exploits, mild though they had been, lost nothing in the telling. Customers fell off. To be sure, his many cousins, with the exception of the shameless Joazar, put kinship first. But the actual difference between prosperity and privation was small. It was soon seen that Nathaniel lost weight and did not look well. Nor was he as genial as he used to be. Instead of joking with his customers as they came in, he wearied their patience with complaints against his cousin Joazar.

He knew that Joazar had the bees. It was not a very good season, and he sold what honey he gathered because he needed money. He was sinking into a state of sour despair, his temperament curdled by dwelling on his grievance. As sometimes happens, the possession of an enemy was transforming him from a kindly, superficially pleasant man into something more complex, more disagreeable. What he was, he did not know. Indeed, till this moment it had not occurred to him to wonder. Now he fell to brooding and neglected work. Unless he were careful, more customers would desert him. He knew it, yet a ferment inside himself seemed to paralyze action.

All this came to a head when his daughter Tabitha, with a smile which she had not often worn of late, set before him his favorite dish of figs steeped in honey. Such a luxury was beyond his reach these days, and his mouth watered for it. But the honey . . .

A sudden, intolerable suspicion came over him, and he scowled at his daughter. "Where did you get this honey?"

She was actually eager to tell him. "No, it is not ours, Father. I did not keep any back. I could not disobey you. It was given — and I am sure for the healing of all quarrels — and it was generous of him, was it not — by Joazar."

Nathaniel picked up the dish and hurled it out of the doorway, where it shattered against Tabitha's oven, leaving a trail of figs and honey over the floor. Then he got to his feet and boxed Tabitha's ears, first one side then the other. "Take that for a fool!" he said, quivering. "How dared you? My own bees, and he insults me with a little jar of honey! O-oh!" He put

up his hands to his hair and tugged at it. He had to do
something, and Tabitha had fled in tears. He knew
exactly how it had been, how Joazar had sent him the
honey in a mocking spirit to assure him that he did
indeed have the bees. He wanted to knock Joazar
down and trample on him. He wanted . . . ah, he
knew now what he had been thirsting for — not satisfaction, not even reparation, but revenge!

Poor little Tabitha, timidly peering at him in hope
that she might tiptoe past unobserved, was forced to
linger in the court because her father was walking up
and down, muttering strangely to himself.

There had been a preacher in town of late, very
different from good old Rabbi Jehuda or even from
the younger Rabbi Gorion, whose insistence was on
fine details of the Law. He was a traveling man, this
Rabbi Hezekiah, if rabbi indeed he was. He had moved
up from Judaea because he had attracted dangerous notice there. He was now beginning to find even Galilee
too hot to hold him, so that he came close up to the
border where he could slip over if need be into Perea.
King Agrippa's government had by no means welded
these provinces into one, so that it was possible for a
man to be safe here and not there, unless King Agrippa
had taken the trouble to issue definite orders.

Whatever Rabbi Hezekiah's credentials, he was impressive. His fiery eloquence was a far different thing
from the trembling kindness of the dear old rabbi, or
even from the dry logic of Rabbi Gorion. It was a fact,
moreover, that he came from Jerusalem, where it

seemed that indignation against the carelessness of the
High Priests and those in office was raising up a new
generation of prophets in Israel. It was only natural
that the synagogue elders should have been impressed,
though Rabbi Jehuda shook his white head in dismay
and Rabbi Gorion looked down his long nose at
Hezekiah's credentials. Hezekiah's preaching had
made the congregation sit up. Everybody knew what
the dear old rabbi would say, while Gorion went in one
ear and out the other, edifying in a vague way by his
learning, but seldom remembered. Hezekiah was
frightening, burning, insistent, uncomfortable. He was
afire with hatred of Romans, of gentiles, and especially of sinners whose lukewarmness had hardened the
heart of the Lord to be angry with Israel. He was in
fact a great cursing rabbi. The fragments of scripture
which rose to Nathaniel's mind as he thought of his
cousin were of a kind to which he had never listened
until lately. And of all sinners in Israel were not pub-
licans the worst because they served the government,
be it heathen or half-Jew? So said Hezekiah, calling on
the faithful to cast out from their midst the evil ones.

Before the swarming of the bees, this turgid eloquence would have made small impression on Nathaniel. He was easygoing and unused to thinking
about disturbing things. He was trained, however, to
accept the words of his spiritual leaders; and he was
learning to hate. Small wonder that the two coalesced
in his mind, so that his duty to destroy the publican
had been revealed to him together with the desire.

These were the latter days, and the Lord was demand-
ing great works from each of His people. It was no
longer sufficient to ply one's trade and walk in the Law.

Nathaniel had experienced a religious conversion, if
of a peculiar kind. It had really flashed into his mind
that the Lord had called him, Nathaniel, personally to
do this thing. He felt himself a man transformed — not,
to be sure, by exaltation, but by the consciousness of a
fixed purpose. Hitherto religion, though it had guided
his whole life, had been impersonal and simple. Nothing had been asked of him that he could not do, and
especially nothing that was not also demanded of his
neighbors.

He had no thought of violence, since it was not in
his nature. It never occurred to him that a stout club
or a quick knife might do the Lord's work. But, starting from the premise that the publican was wicked,
he conceived it as his duty to expose him. The consequence would be that Joazar, cast out of the congregation, probably beaten, would be known and exe-
crated for what he was. Driven out of the town, reduced to beggary, he might wander the land, another
Ishmael, living evidence that Israel was purifying her-
self in preparation for the mighty works which the
Lord would do against the heathen.

Such pictures were very vague in Nathaniel's mind.
He did not dwell on them or puzzle what they meant.
He did not need to, since the outline of his own conduct in the situation was clear. To expose the iniqui-
ties of Joazar, he must first discover them. It was use-

less to complain of his own wrongs or even in general of Joazar's profession. People already knew about both. Heads were shaken certainly, yet Joazar was and would be tolerated. Was it not whispered that he had done some very convenient favors? It would be necessary to catch him in some horrifying act, some piece of blasphemy or double-dealing which could not be excused. Nathaniel did not doubt that he could do this. Was he not the instrument which the Lord had chosen for this purpose?

It is a hard thing to ask of a petty tradesman that he loiter away his business hours in the market or the wineshop for the purpose of keeping an unobstrusive eye on a collector of customs. A man must live, and Nathaniel soon decided that there was nothing to be learned by watching his cousin. He intercepted, to be sure, a few quick glances or nods of understanding. Their significance did not escape him, and yet it did not much interest him either. It was understood that men like Joazar took under-counter tips. How else would they live? Surely not on the miserable percentage which those who contracted for the taxes would allow them. It was evident, it is true, that Joazar's connections were made impartially with Jews or gentiles. Something might possibly in the end develop from this, but not in the market place in open day. Puzzled perhaps, but not unhopeful, Nathaniel went back to his shop and his business.

It might be more profitable to keep watch on Joazar's house at night. People did come to see him, but it was difficult to be sure who they were or for what reason they came. Joazar was a sociable man, and the sound of his laughter often floated out into the street as Nathaniel passed by. But the very fact that there were comings and goings made it impossible to lurk near his doorway. Even on moonless nights the stars were luminous, while a visitor for any dark purpose would be bound to cast a suspicious eye into corners.

Many days went past, and Nathaniel was no closer to a great discovery. He was not in general a man whose impressions were lasting, and he might in normal circumstances have cooled off. It chanced, however, that Rabbi Hezekiah still lingered. King Agrippa was openly courting the favor of the Pharisees who had groaned under the Roman rule in Judaea. Thus even the extremists of that party were tolerated by his orders, though it was evident that they were not to be won over. King Agrippa was earning favor by a more popular persecution, that of the followers of Jesus, who were causing scandal to the pious by fellowship with gentiles and disregard of the Law. Rabbi Hezekiah, though skirting dangerously the charge of treason, had so far been left alone. He had begun preaching not only in the synagogue, but outside it. Whenever Nathaniel felt his ardor slackening, it was possible to listen to the rabbi and be refreshed.

Still, something new had to be done. It took Nathaniel quite some time to work himself up to the point of spending money. Eventually, however, and with many sighings at what he knew could be but ill-afforded, he bribed his cousin Levi to let him watch Joazar's yard from a nearby rooftop.

Almost at once he felt he had discovered something, though it was hard to feel satisfaction when the money which he had laid out was needed to buy leather. There were nights when those who knocked at Joazar's door came in cheerfully and spent the evening with him. There were others when they spoke with him low-voiced in the gate and did not enter. Sometimes when Joazar recrossed his yard on these occasions, one might have supposed he walked heavily as though he carried something. In the darkness, Nathaniel could not be sure of this or see the faces of those who came and went, who heralded their coming with a peculiar knock — three heavy strokes, three quick ones.

He had stumbled without a doubt on a smuggling ring a little larger than one might have supposed — a group of merchants whose extra profits depended on the blind eye of the tax collector. Nathaniel was aware of this, yet he dismissed it as pure irrelevance. There was no provision in God's Law for paying customs duties. It followed therefore that their evasion was no crime. He might have tried the effect of denouncing his cousin to Agrippa's officer-in-charge, but he never considered this. God had commanded him to expose Joazar's wickedness, not his disobedience to a set of regulations which did not matter.

This being so, there must be more involved in Joazar's secret connections than a little harmless prof-iteering. There must be something vicious, if he could

but probe it. It was useless to sit on a nearby roof and
watch dim shadows murmuring together. If he could
but see and hear!

He thought of that olive tree in Joazar's yard, thick
and gnarled. It would be easy climbing. But Joazar's
yard was walled all round, as was a common custom
where houses were crowded very close together. There
were always fig trees to protect from neighboring
goats, or a crop of olives which would be worth
stealing. The cheap brickwork would flake easily, so
that one could hardly scramble across without causing
a rattle. Whatever would he say if he were caught? If
it were imagined that he had taken to burglary, stripes
and disgrace would be his own portion. By no means
confident in the protection of the Holy One when it
came to this point, Nathaniel was frightened.

He was driven on by lack of money and the fear of
further expense. The madness which gnawed at him
had already suggested that a discreet bribe here and
there might bring information. That way lay certain
ruin. He could not afford it. It would be better to risk
the wall and the olive tree, though the very thought
of them brought his heart into his mouth. Besides, he
knew he could not bear the strain of the Lord's work
very much longer. People had begun to look at him
in a queer way. When he passed, they put their heads
together. He did not need to turn round and catch
them at it. He could feel them.

He was standing on an upturned basket in the corner
of Levi's yard, head and shoulders over Joazar's wall.

To the right of him, and only just out of reach, the olive tree cut off the gate from view. Joazar's doorway, inside of which his lamp glimmered dully, was ahead of him and to the left, a few yards off. The house was quiet, for all the world as though Joazar, like his neighbors, went early to bed. Yet Joazar was awake and listening. How was it possible to get in sight or even within earshot of that gate? Nathaniel was actually frozen to the spot because his basket creaked at the slightest move.

The night was not quiet, of course. It never was. Owls hooted. A man and his wife were yelling at each other. A baby was crying. There were murmurs of distant conversations carried on from rooftops, where people sat to catch the evening air. But Levi was asleep, and the house of Joazar was quiet as a tomb. Here the slightest sound stood out at once from its background of distant noise. Already Joazar had moved into his doorway to listen. Nathaniel had not seen him, but his shadow obscured the light of the lamp. He was standing motionless while Nathaniel clutched the wall and held his breath. He dared not so much as duck his head out of sight, lest the basket creak.

Someone knocked at the gate quickly, urgently. It was neither the signal of Joazar's secret visitors nor yet the thumping of his familiar friends. Joazar himself found it strange, for he moved over the threshold into Nathaniel's line of vision and said sharply, but pitching his voice low, "Who's that?"

It was lucky that he looked straight at the gate

without glancing sideways to where Nathaniel's head, faintly visible against the starry sky, stared terrified at him.

The man outside did not answer Joazar but merely knocked again, hardly more than tapping with his fingers, but with the same anxious haste.

Joazar appeared to hesitate, and in a moment the tapping broke out again for the third time.

"I come," Joazar said, and moved past the olive tree out of Nathaniel's sight.

He lifted the bar which held the gate at night, and it creaked back. There was hasty whispering. Nathaniel, who was far closer than he had ever been before, strained every nerve to listen. It was useless. The very murmur of the stranger's voice was hard to catch, as though he had actually put his mouth close up to Joazar's ear. Joazar's answers, though audible for the most part, were brief. "Indeed it is a long time . . . Perhaps. I do not know . . . I have connections." There followed another long muttering from the stranger, after which Joazar said, though it was clear he hesitated slightly, "Well . . . come in!"

The gate creaked to. The bar was gently lowered, and the two men came padding past the olive tree, Joazar leading. The man who followed was slender and short, but there was nothing more to be told from his vague outline. He halted, however, in the light of the doorway and, putting back his headcloth, raised his face to Joazar, smiling as if to say, "Before I enter, look on me in the light of the lamp. I really am the person

I have claimed to be." In answer, Joazar put a hand on his arm and drew him in.

The door shut tight. Nathaniel climbed cautiously down to the ground on legs that wobbled and lowered himself to a sitting position. He trembled all over. He, too, knew the man; and there was a price on his head. He had not altered much, and there had been a period when his face was as well-known in town as Joazar's own. He likewise had been a collector of customs, this . . . Matthew, who had left town with the Rabbi Jesus. Now he was on the run and making for the border, so that naturally he had thought of Joazar and the little connections which customs people have.

There were legends still in town about Rabbi Jesus, though it was now known he had been a false prophet. But his followers were far worse than he. They trampled on the Covenant which God had made with Moses and his people. Even King Agrippa had vowed to exterminate these, while Hezekiah, that servant of the Lord, had cursed them terribly. The very hair on Nathaniel's head seemed to bristle at the thought of the wickedness he had been so close to.

As for Joazar, why, the Lord had delivered him into Nathaniel's hand! A word to the captain of King Agrippa's guard, and Joazar would come to a bad end. It was not that Nathaniel desired or ever expected to drag the guard into this business. But they could not now be kept out. Joazar's iniquity had touched King

Agrippa himself. There was no help for it.

Nathaniel sat a long time in the dust of the yard, trying to nerve himself to face the soldiers. These men
were not Jews, and they were rough with people who
attracted their attention. Little tradesmen did not like
to be mixed up with them on any pretext. He could
not venture to wake them in the middle of the night.
He must wait till the morning. This reflection at
least gave him the fortitude to get up and go home, but
he did not sleep well. Things he did not like to think
of rose before him in that unguarded time between
sleeping and waking when the conscious mind loses
control.

It was a long time ago, when Nathaniel had been a
small boy, that his uncle Sapphias had gone off to fight
for the Holy One. He remembered his uncle Sapphias
well, for he lived with them and was glad to toss small
boys in the air when they begged him to do so. This
uncle Sapphias had gone to fight for the Lord under
Judas of Galilee, who was raising a rebellion just then
against the Romans and was spoken of everywhere
as a deliverer. Nathaniel had been proud of his uncle;
and even his father, though he looked grave, had allowed the women to indulge in boasting.

But there came a day when his mother was in tears
and his sisters were wailing and his father threw ashes
on his head. It frightened him; but when he asked the
reason, they would not say. Very shortly, as little
children will, he pieced it together. His uncle Sapphias

was caught by the Romans and crucified.

Crucified!

He had known quite well what the word meant, but he had not been able to connect it with his uncle Sapphias. His imagination hinted nightmare things, but he could not understand them. He would wake up screaming and be unable to say why. After some months of this, he could not bear his thoughts any longer and had decided that he would see for himself. He had run away to watch an execution.

What he had seen, he never thought of now. There were people who went to watch these things out of curiosity or personal involvement or perverted pleasure. As for Nathaniel, he had never so much as been past the place since. He had never even gone out of that gate of the town which led to it. The details of that sight had completely faded. Or he thought they had. They began to come back to him . . . the brutal soldiery driving the victim on with blows, that man who might have been his uncle, might have been Matthew, might have been Joazar!

With a jerk, Nathaniel was wide awake, sitting upright in his bed. The horrible details which lurked in his memory were clearer to him than they had been since childhood. He tried to banish them but could not. He convinced himself that they had no relevance to the fate of Matthew or of Joazar, but he did not lie down again. He did not want to fall asleep.

He was at work very early. There was no knowing

how long the soldiers would detain him, and it was
prudent to get a few things finished first. No point
in losing custom to his rival down the street. Presently
a customer came in, needing to be measured for shoes.
Then came another with the girth-strap of his donkey,
which was broken.

There was still plenty of time, and business was business. Nathaniel bustled about until the midday meal
was ready. He would certainly not dare wake the
soldiers from their siesta. He put off his visit until the
sun was lower.

During siesta when he was trying to make up for his
lost night, words came unbidden into his mind, in-
spired quite possibly by the soporific murmur of the
bees. A voice seemed to say in his head, "The theft of
a hive is no good reason for you to betray your cousin."

He sat up and took himself to task. The bees had
nothing, or very nearly nothing to do with the matter.
It had been laid upon him to unmask the wickedness of
Joazar, and he had done so. Was it his fault that the
consequences bade fair to be drastic? Assuredly Rabbi
Hezekiah would not say so.

When siesta time was over, he went out. He did not,
however, turn his steps toward the guardhouse, but
to the market. Here in the shadow of the city gate,
Rabbi Hezekiah was wont to sit and talk to all who
would listen.

The market was nearly empty, as it always was in
the afternoon. Joazar was still there, but Rabbi

Hezekiah had left. Nathaniel's heart fell. He despaired of nerving himself to do what he ought to do without the rabbi.

He caught a passerby by the mantle. "Where is Rabbi Hezekiah?"

The fellow winked and jerked his thumb. "Over the border! He had word from the captain of the guard he had better get out." He spat contemptuously. "They did not want to arrest him, but when they heard him . . . Did *you* hear him?"

"I heard him," Nathaniel said.

The man dug him in the ribs. "You know, then. Troublemaker. Now the real Jerusalem rabbis, they say, hold with King Agrippa."

"Oh, yes," said Nathaniel blankly. Absorbed in his own affairs, he had never heard such cavalier dismissal of the rabbi.

"And so do I," insisted the man. "And why not, eh?"

He thrust his face close to Nathaniel's, smelling of garlic.

"Why not?" agreed Nathaniel weakly. In the presence of the very guard by the gate, what else could he say? Nor was he a revolutionary. It would never occur to him to rise and fight for the Lord like his uncle Sapphias.

"That's right, then," said the man. "Thought for a moment you were one of the fools who used to listen to him."

He turned away, and Nathaniel crept home deflated.

Since, however, the setting of the sun would bring the Sabbath, it was apparent there was no hurry. Joazar, in the market place all day, would have had no time to make arrangements, nor would Matthew have dared to move before the setting of the sun. And he would not travel on the Sabbath. It was safe for Nathaniel to put the matter off.

He was still doing this on the Sabbath morning when the time for synagogue came. He could not admit to himself that he was not going to the guardhouse in his own good time. But he would not fix on any definite moment. Uneasily he was relapsing into his normal habit of deferring unpleasant things. His fierce resentment against his cousin had quite disappeared. Indeed, when he thought of it, he perceived that it had gone long ago. But the duty which had been laid on him and the words of Hezekiah — ah, these were different things. He did not want to face them, and yet neither could he turn his back on them. He did not dare to, for the anger of the Holy One was terrifying to think of.

Synagogue without Rabbi Hezekiah was extraordinarily tame. All the familiar faces were in the elders' chairs. There was not even, as there so often was, a visiting worthy. The president gave the scrolls to Rabbi Jehuda, who read in his trembly old voice a passage from Isaiah. Very old indeed was Rabbi Jehuda, so that his head nodded as he spoke and the scrolls drooped in his hand. Indeed, it was common knowledge that he recited the sacred words by heart, for his eyes were failing. Some said his memory was going, too; but if he stumbled, it did not matter. He read in Hebrew, while the congregation listened to the voice of the interpreter in Aramaic. "Comfort ye, comfort ye, my people," read the rabbi, as he must have done a thousand times in that same room. He closed the scrolls and settled himself in his chair, while the congregation on the floor before him prepared to listen respectfully to the same words as usual.

The rabbi fingered his straggly beard, and he paused for a very long moment until it flashed into more than one mind that he had forgotten what it was he always said. There was a strained hush over the room while the opening words, "It is written . . ." formed themselves silently on many lips. But the rabbi did not use them.

"My children," said the rabbi, leaning forward and fixing his nearly sightless eyes on the formless shadows of the people before him, "you have heard it told how in Jerusalem the disciples of the great rabbis will defend their masters' doctrines with sticks and stones, one school against another. I myself have seen a promising lad lie dead, a true son of Israel — and he that killed him was no less zealous for the Law. The matter at issue was the pouring of the water by the priest at the great festival — should it be done by him or no. Now if the disputes of the rabbis engender such heat that lives are lost upon the matter, does it follow that one school is in the right and another wrong? I tell you, no. For the matter may not be decided by the Council until all arguments have been threshed out. Thus for the present the disagreement of the schools is lawful, and the zeal of one side is as pleasing to the Lord as that of the other, save for the sticks and stones, which are pleasing to no one.

"In this way Israel is filled with disputes, and many opinions are lawful. For before we obey, we must understand; and before we understand, we must argue. All things are written for us in the Law, yet not all plainly. Much thinking is required before the Council may pronounce on the mind of God.

"It may happen to us, therefore, that a man may visit us speaking boldly of anger and blood and wrath against sinners. Indeed, there are terrible things in the Law, as we have lately been hearing. If they were not in the Law, my children, I would have told you.

"There may be another among us who speaks differently, but is not for that reason outside the Law. It was in this very place a man once told us, 'Love your enemies.' I mean the Rabbi Jesus, whom we all remember. Does not Jacob, who was healed of the palsy by him, sit with us today?"

There was a great silence in the room because the voice of the rabbi was faint, and everyone strained to hear his words. But though no stir was made, looks of astonishment passed up and down the room. It was many years since the name of Rabbi Jesus had been spoken in synagogue.

"Now what this Jesus later did, we all know. And his disciples we know, who think themselves above the

Law. Yet when he did speak within the Law, shall we not remember? And when we think of his end, shall we forget that other people who have also spoken to us and gone away may err through pride, supposing themselves more righteous and more learned than they are?

"Let us then keep this saying, too, in our hearts, not resorting to violence, as the disciples of the great rabbis do, but persisting in neighborly kindness, as being all bound together by the Law. For it is written . . ."

The congregation stirred and began to whisper. They knew precisely what was written and how the rabbi would expound it, since the discourse on neighborly kindness was the one he always gave. But the familiar words were given point by contrast to what he had just told them. People might say that Rabbi Jehuda was senile, but they still revered him above all living men. Small wonder, therefore, that the followers of Hezekiah looked at the ground while Jacob — he who had been cured of the palsy — had tears in his eyes.

There were tears in the eyes of Nathaniel also, tears of relief that he need not betray anyone. He could forget Hezekiah and put the wrath of the Lord aside, relapsing into his easy ways. Had not the rabbi said so? He would fall asleep by his fig trees this afternoon and . . . involuntarily he stirred. He did not want to dream of honey.

All the same, the release was exquisite. He actually

found pleasure as he walked home in nodding at his neighbors, even noticed that they were eager to say a friendly word. It occurred to him that his rival shoemaker had two sons, while he had none. The younger was a personable lad. If Tabitha liked him . . . but not unless she did. His natural benevolence, like a plant which has been cut back, was eager to put out new shoots. This evening he would saunter down the street and turn in at a neighbor's. Not improbably he would take a little wine.

He entered his own yard, looking carelessly around it with pleasurable approval as he used to do. The figs were good this year, for the rains had been heavy. The bees . . .

He still did not want to glance at the bees, but he made himself do so. He blinked and looked again. Impossible! Where there had been three pipes, now there were four. That which had been stolen on the Sabbath in synagogue time had now returned to him in the same way! Joazar knew gentiles who did not keep the Sabbath, and they could have done it for him — but why? What in the world had happened to Joazar?

He stared and stared, unable to believe it. He took a turn up and down the yard and stared again. That Joazar should see the error of his ways might seem incredible, but it had come to pass. And just at the moment when he was harboring that wicked man! Nathaniel bit his finger, thinking it over.

Presently Tabitha called him from the doorway.

"Father, will you not come and eat?"

Nathaniel hesitated and then shook his head. "Presently. Presently I will come, but for the moment I am going to pay a call on our cousin Joazar!"

THE ❋ ❋ ❋ ❋
PEACEMAKER

THE TROUBLE began when the restaurant of Nicolaus was opened up in the house beside the entrance to the Jewish synagogue. Nicolaus himself was a Syrian from Tarsus, and his sausages were not kosher. They smelled, to be sure neither better nor worse than those of Simeon, who was the Jewish sausage seller down street. Both of them catered to the tenement poor who had nowhere to cook or to the sailors of the port. But the shop of Nicolaus was open on the Sabbath, while a restaurant is of all places the most offensive to its neighbors. People do not by any means always carry their food home but eat either in the street or at the proprietor's table, which is in itself always edging out of its awning into the roadway. Thus the shop of Nicolaus was a weekly offense to the pious, whose noses were affronted by the smell of pork, while their persons were forced, as it were, to run the gantlet. Nicolaus's customers, naturally offended at being despised for filthiness, took pleasure in putting themselves in people's way, spitting into the roadway, or indulging in indecent mocking gestures. It was not very long before a deputation from the Jewish synagogue waited upon Nicolaus for the purpose of buying him out.

Nicolaus, who wore on his hairy chest a little replica of the great statue of Artemis at Tarsus, was no lover of Jews. He was indeed an initiate of the spring rites at the Artemis temple, where the people in drunken, beastly ecstasies reverted to primitive sex orgies. This being his conception of religion, he very naturally did not believe in the nameless, shapeless, all-seeing presence of the God of the Jews. He did not even suppose that the Jews did so either, but imagined that they secretly worshipped a god so utterly shameful that they did not dare reveal it. Nicolaus, in fact, was just as contemptuous of the superior ways of the Jews as his customers were. He was, however, in business for his own advantage. If the Jews had offered a good price, putting up meanwhile with the insolence of his tone in negotiations, they could have bought him out.

Unfortunately, the Jewish elders were not tactful. They had actually included in their deputation Simeon, who was Nicolaus's rival. This was in itself a regrettable error, while Simeon's character made it worse. He and Nicolaus were two of a kind. Big, burly, loudmouthed, equally intolerant, they had already done more to divide the street, and even the quarter, into two enemy camps than had been accomplished by the frictions of ten years. On this occasion, they had but to meet to set up a quarrel, Simeon at pains to express his loathing of pork, and Nicolaus threatening to purify the Jew in hot, greasy water if he did not remove his filthy presence. The meeting broke up in confusion without even naming a preliminary price to haggle over.

After that, Nicolaus's behavior was much worse. There were always obstructions in the narrow roadway. During synagogue, he would lead his customers in the caterwauling of ribald songs, while beating on the table and clashing pots and pans as an accompaniment. These tactics were actually good for trade, since Jew-baiting appealed to the rowdies of the port. A Sabbath morning with Nicolaus was as good as a play; and long before synagogue opened, his table was crowded.

Naturally, the Jews were no less aggressive. Caesarea, founded by the great Herod and endowed with an amphitheatre, a temple of Rome and Augustus, and other public buildings in the heathen style, was not beloved of Jews. All the same, it was the residence of the Roman governor and in consequence administrative center of Judaea. Many Jews lived there, perforce, and they all considered it, unloved though it was, as their own town. Jewish rowdies were just as common as pagan ones and more fanatical. Stones were whizzed at Nicolaus; filth was tossed into his restaurant. On one occasion his customers came down with a vomiting and sickness of the bowels which he attributed not to his sausage but to something which an enemy had slipped into his cauldrons.

This final stroke embittered Nicolaus, since it affected his business. For the first time since his feud with the Jews had commenced, his shop was empty. In spite of the profits which he had lately made, his resources were not large. If such an episode were to be often repeated, he would be ruined. The thought galled Nicolaus almost as much as it frightened him. His demonstrations against the Jews hitherto had been rough and unpleasant, but they had stopped short of physical harm. People had been insulted, forced to walk over dirty ground, disturbed at their devotions. In fact, they had been targets of what among cruder folk passed for Nicolaus's sense of humor. By now, however, he was ready for violence. All that restrained him was the knowledge that, were he to start a riot, his own shop would be the first to be leveled to the ground.

Nicolaus, as it chanced, belonged to a burial club which had been founded under the patronage of Artemis for the purpose of saving up for decent interment of its members. In the course of doing so, it held monthly meetings where a dinner was consumed, dues were collected, and religious rites performed. It was, in fact, a poor man's club, which under the influence of Nicolaus was becoming, at every meeting, more anti-Jewish.

"I hate them!" he would say, setting the ball rolling after dinner as they sat over their wine.

Loucas, who was a potter of sorts, making small terra-cotta images of the gods and cheap little amulets, rejoined that all Jews had the Evil Eye. What their

philters and potions would do, moreover, was well
known. Many a person had lost his life or reason
through them; and he did not doubt that this would
have happened to Nicolaus, too, had he not been protected by the amulet of the goddess. Nicolaus, belch-
ing sonorously, agreed.

"They worship an ass," Ptolemaius assured them.
"I heard it from a sailor who had it from one of their
priests that he saved from drowning. There is actually
a monster with an ass's head set up in their Holy of
Holies, but this is a secret jest played on them by their
priests. The rest of the people do not know what their
god really is."

Everybody guffawed at the thought of this jest on
the people. Ptolemaius owned a couple of strong slaves
whom he rented out as stevedores in the docks, and for
that reason he was the best-informed man present. Sailors, as is well known, will tell you anything; so that
to rub shoulders with them is an education.

"Now it stands to reason," said Gorgias the leather
worker, who had been brooding silently hitherto, "that
a piece of good pigskin will make as strong a strap or
stout a shoe as other leather."

Nicolaus grunted agreement. His chief objection,
and indeed that of them all to the Jews, was the Jewish
refusal to deal with gentile tradesmen. Why, Jewish
women would not so much as borrow a measure of meal
from a gentile neighbor!

The conversation broke down into anecdote with

several talking at once. Each of the company had a story about his own particular Jewish rival and wanted to tell it, even though nobody listened.

Loucas, the image maker, a persistent little man, brought them back onto a general theme. If the Jews would not buy his wares, it was their own loss. What he objected to was not their refusing the protection of the gods, but their interference with the pious practices of other people.

Ptolemaius reminded them that everywhere in the world the gods were worshipped, perhaps under local forms and names, but what of that? The Jews alone set their face against obvious truth.

Why, they would not, put in Demetrius, who had not spoken yet, so much as allow the image of the emperor to be set up.

There was a shocked silence. Everybody had known this fact, but the solemn reminder from Demetrius had drawn fresh attention to it. Naturally emperors were men, and, unlike Artemis, they were limited by human nature. They died, for instance. While they were on earth, they could not be invisibly present in many places at once, as Artemis was. Yet while this was perfectly clear, even to the ignorant, it also went without saying that the emperor's power was more than an ordinary man's. In appreciation of this fact, it was proper and loyal to set up the emperor's image and burn incense to it. Nobody, not even Demetrius, who was known to be stupid, confused this emperor-worship with that of his own favorite god and protector. Yet while the refusal of a man to worship the gods might be his own affair, to reject the emperor was clear subversion.

"Everyone knows they hate the government," growled Nicolaus, passing a hand through his mane of hair which was crisply curling and jet black. "If they had their own way, they would drive us all out of Judaea."

"And out of the whole East," agreed Ptolemaius. "It is what they talk of in their synagogues on their Sabbath. If people had any sense at all, they'd not allow it."

"That's all very well," objected Nicolaus. "In a riot, my shop's next door, while yours is down the street."

"Once you bring out the soldiers," Loucas agreed, "everybody gets hurt."

There was silence while the others pondered this undeniable truth.

"In Alexandria," said Ptolemaius thoughtfully, "a sailor told me, various people set the emperor's statue in some of their synagogues. Since they dared not, because of the disrespect, cast those images out, they deserted the places."

Nicolaus put his head back and went into a great peal of laughter. "The emperor's image! Then they deserted the place. Friends, we'll do it!"

The idea caught on with a hubbub of approval which presently resolved itself into a discussion of ways and means. The young emperor had not been reigning long, with the consequence that demands for his statue far exceeded the supply. To be sure, an image need not be a portrait. Any young man with "Gaius Caesar" written on the base would certainly do. But Apollos and similar available statues were nearly always naked, which would not be respectful for the emperor. Ptolemaius ingeniously suggested that the head of an Apollo might be removed from its torso and made to do. A bust of Gaius would be easier to handle than a statue, especially as the plan was to introduce it secretly into the synagogue by night. As Loucas was quick to point out, the Roman governor would severely punish any act which led to race riots.

So far all was clear, but even a bust of Gaius thus faked was not easy to obtain. Nobody had the money to buy a marble statue of Apollo. It was suggested that Loucas make a bust of terra-cotta, but he shook his head. His kilns, he asserted, were too small. It had become evident that Loucas was afraid of the whole business.

Gorgias now gave the plan a new lease on life by remarking that his cousin worked for a stonemason. He would make inquiries.

This was assented to, and the meeting broke up, pleasantly heated by wine and discussion. Nicolaus, who had undertaken to break into the synagogue, had rapidly concluded that this could not be done through the walls, which were too thick, or the doors, which were very heavy. In the façade, however, was a great window, high up and obscured by a grating, yet possible for a slim man to wriggle through. Nicolaus in person was too large for the job; but among his customers were twin brothers, jugglers by trade, who he imagined would not be above a little housebreaking if well rewarded. Unlike the others in the plot, Nicolaus was actually prepared to put out money.

The matter rested at about this stage for a month, largely owing to the difficulty of finding a suitable statue. By this time, the project had become widely known in the quarter, since Nicolaus was not intelligent enough to be discreet. Had the separation between the gentiles and Jews been less complete, some rumor must surely have betrayed the matter. In the poorer quarters of the city, however, people traded exclusively with their own kind and were able to do so because their expenditures were simple and their businesses quite small. The plot of Nicolaus, which was sniggered at everywhere in gentile houses or shops, remained a secret from Jews living in the same street.

By the next full meeting of the club, which Loucas discreetly did not attend, Nicolaus had a stonemason busy altering a bearded head of Zeus to a rough likeness of the smooth cheeks and close-cropped hair of the new emperor. The work was not paid for and not likely to be so soon, but the stonemason for the sake of such a jest would wait for his money.

On these terms the matter was arranged for the next moonless night. Gorgias and Demetrius were to keep watch on the street; while Ptolemaius, who lived a few doors off, held a noisy party for other members of the club. This would provide cover for scuffling out of doors or coming and going past the synagogue. Meanwhile Nicolaus and his twin helpers, aided by a ladder and long ropes, would do the deed.

In this way the bust was successfully planted, not just before the Sabbath, as Nicolaus would have preferred, but when the weather was right. The following morning, Nicolaus's restaurant was suspiciously crowded, while other people who could not leave their shops popped into the roadway as opportunity served. The whole quarter was agog when, punctual to his moment, the Jewish attendant came down to open the building for the school.

It all went perfectly. He entered solemnly, every hair in place, and then came bursting out as if shot from a catapult, his features working, his headgear slipped to one side. Without saying anything, he disappeared up the street at a run, his sandals pattering and his elbows working with unaccustomed effort. Behind him, he left the doors of the synagogue wide open so that the curious could peer inside at the bust of Gaius, small and pallid, mounted square beside the chest in which they kept their sacred scrolls.

Inside the restaurant, people rolled with laughter, slapped Nicolaus on the back, roared witticisms, and ventured out to have a look at Gaius, whose sculptured lips smiled blandly on his new home. Within minutes, however, the commotion about the synagogue also attracted an agitated crowd of Jews, who broke into wailing when they saw the dreadful thing. Those

among them who retained their presence of mind
slammed the doors. Others, more imprudent, answered
the mockery of the crowd with angry shouts. By the
time the elders of the synagogue arrived panting, pieces
of mud brick had begun to whizz back and forth. In
fact, a riot was only hindered by the difficulty of sepa-
rating sides in the narrow streets and perhaps also by the
mixed nature of the crowd. There were women and
children caught up in it. Besides, many of the Jews
were more concerned with shrieking wildly, tearing
their hair or garments, scoring their faces than they
were with taking vengeance. That would come later.

The elders of the synagogue, finding it impossible to
make their way through the street, went round to
an entrance on the other side which was not used by
the public and feasted their eyes on the horrid thing.
They, too, tore their garments and lamented with loud
cries; but, seeing the inscription, they laid no hand on
the bust and ordered the synagogue securely closed,
lest anyone else should venture to do so. Then sallying
forth, they tried to control their congregation.

They were only jostled for their pains. There was
no eminence from which they could be seen except the
rooftops. These, however, were already occupied by
angry people who were pelting their enemies below
them with tiles. The crowd was seething, fresh people hurrying up to impede the efforts of those now
frantic to get away. Here and there an older man or
else a woman stumbled with a shriek and went down
under a swirling heap. The tumult had already over-

flowed the restaurant of Nicolaus, knocked over his
table, snapped the poles of his awning. It was now lap-
ping against the booths further down the street, some
Jewish, some gentile. Their owners, engaged in rescu-
ing what they could, found themselves fighting with
rowdies or sneak thieves who saw the tumult as an opportunity for plunder.

In vain the elders of the synagogue plucked those
whom they could reach by the sleeve. In vain the rabbis, fighting their way onto the rooftops with the
aid of younger disciples, called on the people below
them to go home. Those that heard them could not
get away. In any case, many of the Jews now belonged
to other congregations and did not know the elders of
the district. Racial hatreds, going far beyond the original grievance, were erupting like a volcano. The
synagogue elders might just as well have shouted at
Vesuvius.

Cuspius Fadus, the Roman governor, was not in a
hurry to call his soldiers out. These, being Syrian and
gentiles themselves, were not impartial. Their interference would most probably start off a battle which
would go on for days in the narrow streets, resulting in
a loss of good soldiers and a massacre of Jews. Undoubtedly Fadus would in that case be brought to book
by his superior, the governor of Syria. It was his business to avoid trouble, not provoke it. Fadus, therefore,
temporized while the riot spread. Presently, the cry of
fire was raised at one point, then another. There were
plenty of braziers in the little workshops, which were

easily upset by any struggle. In the absence of an
abundant water supply, fires spread, absorbing the efforts of first one group, then another. Jew and gentile,
threatened equally by the flames, fought side by side.
The original riot began to break up into groups, allowing such people as had been trapped in the mob to
getaway. Refugees now streamed out of the quarter;
and Cuspius Fadus, who had already cordoned it off,
gave orders to let them by. Thus emptied of people,
the streets became easier to control. Now was the moment for the soldiers to advance under strict discipline,
isolating pockets of disturbance and pushing slowly
toward the synagogue where things had begun.

This maneuver, which took all day and all night, was
finally accomplished with very little loss among the
cohorts. A few hundred Jews and gentiles perished.
Blocks of houses here or there were gutted by fire.
This negligible damage, however, was something Fadus
could afford to boast of. But for his timing, half the
city might have been laid waste, as had recently happened in similar circumstances in Alexandria.

Nevertheless, as Cuspius Fadus took his place on his
chair of state to hear deputations from gentiles and
from Jews, he was only too conscious that the difficult part of his task was yet to come. As Roman governors went, Fadus was not a bad man, reasonably able
and no more corrupt than was acceptable to give him
a decent profit from his labors. It was too much to
hope for that he should regard the religion of his Jewish subjects with anything but contempt. Surprisingly,

however, Fadus despised Greek superstitions as well. A philosopher of the school of the scientific Epicurus, he held that gods were formed of atoms, like everything else, and lived their lives in a separate world. Visions of them seen on earth from time to time were mere visual images which by a millionth chance had passed through intervening space without being broken up. They had no significance, and the gods had no relationship with men. Thus caring nothing for the beliefs of either side, Fadus felt no inner impediment to justice.

Listening to the arguments, his cleanshaven, prosperous face impassive, Fadus was careful to give no sign indicating his decision. In desiring the removal of the image from their synagogue, the Jews were right. Divine Augustus, whose ruling principle it had been that every nation should exercise its own customs freely, had granted permission for the Jews to show their loyalty to Caesar by a daily sacrifice on his behalf in their Temple. Since images of any sort were forbidden to them, they were exempted from putting up his statue. Divine Tiberius, though in many ways less favorable to Jews, had upheld these concessions. As far, therefore, as the law was concerned, it was unnecessary for the Jews to present an argument at all. The Greeks had no case.

These facts were as well known to the Greeks and Jews as they were to Fadus himself. They did not, however, shorten their eloquence. The Jews were anxious to protest their loyalty, lest the young emperor revoke their privilege. If he did so, the nation would revolt, since their Law was dearer to the people than life itself. The Greeks, meanwhile, had much to say about loyalty also. In addition, they hotly defended Nicolaus, a respectable citizen whom the Jews, they said, without any evidence accused of the outrage.

Fadus let them talk themselves out, listening gravely almost like a statue himself in his gold-inlaid chair with the handsome folds of his snow-white toga about him. He was reluctant to have them come to an end, even though at the very beginning he knew what he ought to do. The statue should be removed. As for Nicolaus, whom he held in jail, his soldiers would have no trouble in beating a confession out of him. There was every reason for making an example of him promptly.

So thought the Jews, too, and even the Greeks, whose protestations had been more for the sake of the record than anything else. Yet when Fadus eventually lifted his chin from his hand and gave judgment, what he said came as a surprise. He understood perfectly, Fadus said, the customs of the Jews as well as the privileges which the divine emperors had bestowed on them. As for Nicolaus, if he were satisfied of his guilt, he should be punished promptly. Since, however, the Governor of Syria wished to consult with him at once, it did not become him to decide on any question without asking his superior's view. He would therefore hold the matter over until his return. In the meantime, the synagogue should be closed under guard. Nicolaus should remain in jail while investigations proceeded.

A hubbub of protest arose from the Jews, which Fadus ignored. Gathering his toga about him, he stalked out of the hall, his guard of honor interposing between him and the jubilant Greeks, who counted it victory not to be defeated. Crossing the great court with the fountain and the lesser with the rose garden which lay in his private quarters in the old palace of Herod, Fadus steered a course around the building which brought him by a private way to a little back room, where sat the man who really ruled the province of Judaea.

His name was Faustus, which means Lucky; and he was a freedman or ex-slave of Fadus's own. Like many a ruling Roman who found hard work distasteful, Fadus depended on his secretary in all things. Out of pure self-interest, the man was faithful, since a freedman's fortunes rose and fell with his master's. Fadus therefore trusted him entirely, confiding in him with a lack of reserve which he never dared employ toward his equals. Under Tiberius, too many men had been destroyed by some slight word spoken to an intimate. In Roman circles, a cautious man had no real friends any more.

Fadus sank into a chair and motioned to Faustus to do likewise, for the man had sprung to his feet with an obsequious air which suited his humble condition. When his master had settled himself, and not before, he consented to fold his narrow length onto a stool, rounding his shoulders and bending his head as though, by hunching together, he could emphasize his unimportance. Similarly, he did not speak, but rubbed his hands a little, waiting while Fadus mopped his brow and groaned at the heat.

"I put them off," said Fadus at last with a great sigh. "What else could I do?"

Faustus permitted himself a wry smile, bending forward a little as he spoke in an ingratiating movement. "You could hardly say to them, 'I dare not give the answer that I should because the news has reached me through an unimpeachable source that the emperor is mad.'"

"Stark, staring mad!" Fadus threw out his hands in a despairing gesture. "He has made his horse consul, his sister a goddess. He was always impatient of contradiction, but now . . . ! The slightest hesitation in fulfilling his mad whims is . . . blasphemy! Divine Tiberius, by the gods, was bad enough; but this is mockery! How dare I possibly have this lunatic's image taken from where it has once been set up. He'll have my life!"

"The matter is put off," Faustus consoled him, again making an apologetic bend of his long back. "Meanwhile, something may happen."

"A revolt of the Jews, most likely. Their fanatics will not endure this setback. If by my action I plunge the area in blood, you need not imagine I will be better off — or you either, man."

Faustus smiled at him. "Master, my fortunes are dependent on yours. I seek no other favor. But forgive me, if I do not despair of us both. The pretext, if I say it myself, was an ingenious one which should win time.

You will really go to the governor. During your absence, the Jews will be forced to have patience. They will hardly revolt for a single synagogue, especially as your verdict may still be in their favor."

"And when I return?"

His servant smiled. "I have a plan which may settle the matter. *We* are not superstitious . . ." To please his master, Faustus affected Epicurean doctrines, though actually he had no beliefs at all. "In dealing with these people, we have the advantage that we do not share their delusions."

Fadus laughed. "I see you have a scheme, and it is better that I know nothing of it. But I warn you, if it should go awry, I'll throw you to the wolves!"

Smiling the same fixed smile, his servant answered, "It will not go awry. Yet if it should do so, my life is at your disposal, as it always has been."

"I know, I know." Fadus got up, forcing Faustus to wriggle off his stool and stand humbly before him. "I sometimes wonder if you will not be too clever some day, that is all."

"Ah, but this time," Faustus reminded him, "we are destroyed in any case if you have to give judgment on this affair of the synagogue. It surely is best for me to settle the matter."

"I suppose so." Fadus shrugged unhappily as he turned to go. "Don't say, if you should fail, that I did not warn you."

The servant simply bowed himself again, not straightening until his master had disappeared. Then,

lifting up his eyebrows and pursing his lips in a thoughtful manner, he turned back to the taxes of the province,
which had been engaging his attention when Fadus had
come in. What he thought of his master, he never
permitted himself to say, not even when he supposed
he was alone. For one never knew.

Cuspius Fadus departed in some state for Syria, where
he lingered for a long time. The doors of the
synagogue were sealed with a great seal and guarded by
captains of ten and their detachments from the Syrian
cohort. In the meanwhile, Nicolaus still being in jail,
his cousin Apollos, of whom no one had previously
heard, appeared to look after his business. That he
really was Nicolaus's cousin was evident by the amulet
about his neck and by the fact that he knew all Nicolaus's dirty stories. The arrangement was a sensible
one, since any shop vacant in the quarter was bound to
be plundered. Apollos, who had a breezy way with
him, was soon quite popular even with the soldiers on
guard who, as public servants, considered that they had
a right to free refreshments as long as they did not
abuse the privilege.

It was not long after this that the captain of ten, who
was on duty, one night succumbed to sleep, as did his
whole detachment. Very luckily, Apollos perceived
them lying against the building and woke them up before people came past at dawn to see what had happened. In fact, he helpfully provided a ladder on
which the agitated captain could climb up to peer
through the synagogue window, reassuring himself in

the pale light of dawn that the bust of Gaius was sitting beside the chest of the scrolls undisturbed. Since this was the case and the seals were unbroken, the captain, who had thought perhaps their wine had been drugged, dismissed the notion. He made no report to his superiors. Later, when the miracles commenced, he was afraid to do so.

These started with an awesome burst of music which proceeded from the empty synagogue on the next night. It was the time of the full moon, which is as everybody knows an excellent season for ghosts. The Syrian captain, who wore an amulet against the Evil Eye, went the rounds of the synagogue to encourage his men, stationed about it. Every one of them heard the music, some saying, however, that it appeared to come from deep in the earth. It was not by any means part of their duty that they should encounter devils. Notwithstanding, they stood their ground and held their weapons tight. Reassuringly, the music died out with the same suddenness with which it had arisen.

Early the next morning, their centurion came down in person to visit the guards; and an angry man he was. A bust of Gaius which had never before been there had appeared in the Temple of Rome beside that of the divine Augustus. A rumor already was going around the town that someone or other had removed it from the locked-up synagogue.

A crowd was beginning to gather, under the eyes of which the centurion inspected the unbroken seals and listened to his men. The thing was impossible. They had been awake all night. In brilliant moonlight no one could have traversed the whole town carrying a bust and not be observed. The argument was a good one, yet when the synagogue was finally opened, Gaius had vanished.

The commander of the cohorts, a blunt man to whom miracles were an ingenious trick, replaced Gaius — thereby offending the Jews and those of the Greeks who preferred to think that Gaius, finding himself unfittingly housed, had changed his quarters. He next arrested the guards, without whose connivance, as he pointed out, the bust could not have been removed from the building. He replaced them by a double squad from the Italian cohort, threatening to make short work of any impudent person attempting to repeat the trick. Notwithstanding, after the same mysterious music, the statue, which had as before been locked inside, appeared in the Temple of Rome the following morning.

Public opinion would have left it there, for though the gentiles of the town wished to score off the Jews, the possession of a miracle-working statue was a civic asset by no means to be despised. Besides, the discomfiture of the soldiers, never popular with the people, was gleefully noted. The commander of the cohorts, though frankly mystified, was not disposed to be made a fool of. He replaced the bust once more and stationed his soldiers inside with orders to keep their eyes upon it.

He was awakened early. The guard, as it was re-

ported to him, had been sitting around with their eyes
fixed on Gaius when something had happened. They
did not know what it was, though one or two of them
had noticed a sickly smell. They had awakened from
a trance in the pitch dark, their torches all gone out.
When they had finally managed to rekindle one of
these — well, Gaius was missing.

The commander raged again, but privately he was
a very thoughtful man indeed. Unknown to the guards
inside, he had stationed others, and from a rival cohort,
round the building. It was impossible that the bust
should have been carried out or brought through the
town. To make matters worse, he had also stationed
watchmen about the temple of Rome and Augustus.
Here, however, there was a private way in through
the palace, which abutted on a corner of the sacred
precinct. How the bust ever could have got into the
palace at all, he could by no means conceive. But it
must have done so. The commander was inclined to
keep this knowledge to himself. He felt it wiser.

It was while he was in this state, hesitating between
his dislike of looking a fool and his suspicion that a sensible man would meddle no more with the matter, that
he had a visitor. He did not like Faustus, who had the
reputation of never forgetting a grudge. Since he was
all-powerful with Fadus, the commander feared him
as well as despised him. The servant's cringing manner
made him uneasy. It was like a mask, completely concealing the inner nature of the man. The commander

instinctively looked for some sinister purpose lurking behind it.

On this occasion, Faustus hunched his shoulders and pushed his face close to the commander's, explaining that, knowing how deeply his master Fadus felt on the subject of peace in Caesarea, he had been unable to sleep. If the commander would condescend to explain his course of action, he, Faustus, would be oh so greatly relieved.

The commander nearly choked with mixed emotions. So the slimy creature was at the bottom of it all! He had no further desire to know how the trick was worked. All he wondered was, why. Not having the exclusive information given to the governor about the emperor's mental state, he saw no difficulty in removing the statue from the synagogue if Fadus wished it.

"A miracle-working bust of our dear emperor!" said Faustus, poking his long neck forward with his unmeaning smile. "What a treasure! Presently it will heal a man in a vision, so that other people who are sick will want to touch it. Then it will heal more."

"How do you know?" the commander said.

Not a muscle of the face before him changed, yet now the commander saw the smile as a fixed grin, the teeth bared. "Why, I do not know," Faustus replied. "I only imagine what might just possibly happen. Do you ever amuse yourself, noble Commander, by thinking how a matter may turn out?"

The commander went purple. He was inclined to answer bluntly, no; but he did not dare. He perceived that already he had said the wrong thing and must be more careful. He replied accordingly that it might be better to let the bust decide where it wanted to be. When Fadus returned, he could do what he pleased. If any suspicion were to arise in unworthy minds that the emperor had been insulted by a trick, well, a miracle of healing would undoubtedly put a new face on the matter.

"Just so." Faustus rubbed his bony fingers against his tunic as if he were drying them off. "I felt sure you would see it this way." He smiled again and made his little bow. "Any trick, I imagine, must have had the connivance of the cohorts, must it not? You and I know this could never happen."

The commander of the cohorts swallowed, perceiving that if things went wrong, he was to be the scapegoat. His future, why, even his life might be dependent on putting this miracle over. As Faustus was looking at him inquiringly, he mumbled, "I'll do what I can."

In this way it was that the bust remained in the temple, where it stopped all criticism by performing a miracle of healing almost at once. A few years later, when the mad emperor was murdered, everybody made haste to forget him. The bust then disappeared and was not spoken of again. It was not, however, until after this that the Jews, repairing their synagogue, came on a trapdoor very cunningly concealed in their floor and opening onto a pit which once had been a tunnel communicating with Nicolaus's restaurant. In it, discarded, they found a bust of Gaius, apparent twin to that which had crossed to the temple without being seen in the town. The Jews broke it up into very small pieces and said nothing. Apollos had long ago disappeared overnight from the restaurant, which was now in Jewish possession. Nicolaus himself was thought to have died of jail fever before his innocence or guilt could be established. Strangely, however, there was a dark-haired Syrian in Ephesus for some years after that who called himself Nicolaus and was a devotee of the great Artemis. His existence was known to a few in Caesarea, since characters like Nicolaus are not easily hid. But in what fashion and for what price he bought his freedom from the Romans was not disclosed. Presently he perished from a stone thrown in a riot against a Jewish sect known as the Christians, who were thought to be a menace to the ancient worship of many-breasted Artemis. Even so, he outlived Faustus, who died of a fever, or some said of poison, soon after the return of Cuspius Fadus. He was mourned by his master, who was never as good a governor after that. On his tombstone, Fadus for a whim had inscribed the word, "Peacemaker." It was whispered that since Faustus had never made anything but trouble, the name was ironic.

A ❀ MAN
CALLED
JOHN ❀

A Tale of the Essenes

It was stiflingly hot, even in the shelter of the thick stone walls of the community buildings. Above them the foothills of the Judaean plateau shimmered in the sun, bare, trackless, scored by streambeds of tumbled stone which were bone-dry and blistering to the touch. Below, at the cliff's foot, the dazzling whiteness of salt sands hurt the eye, while the blue waters of the Dead Sea had an oily sheen as though they were composed of molten metal. Nothing visible moved. Even the brethren, who despised the weaknesses of the flesh, had performed their outdoor labors from the dawn hours until noon. Now they went about their business in the shadows, low-voiced, sparing of effort, yet unresting, always conscious that every hour of the day or night a group appointed on behalf of all was studying the Scriptures.

John, keeper of the scrolls, was in the copying

room, where the boy who waited upon him was mixing
ink. Only at such times of day as he was free of
students did John himself unroll the sacred parchments.
No trace of flaw ever marred the manuscripts which
he copied with his own hand. It was his boast that
none had been discovered in his work these thirty years.
He was a tall man, this John, so lean and brown and
wrinkled, so dried out by the sun that it would be difficult to guess at his true age. Hair and beard, bleached
to an indeterminate shade, might once have been red.
The tired eyes were a light gray. His working tunic,
both stained and patched, was held about his middle by
a rope. His feet were bare. But John's movements
were not those of an old man or one beaten down with
toil. Their disciplined slowness had taken on a pride
which was almost regal. As he poured himself water
to purify his hands for the work, he might have been
the High Priest in his golden garments at the Lord's
own altar.

Far different were the movements of the boy. He
perspired, for one thing, and kept passing his hand
across his brow lest the sweat drip off his forehead.
Every so often he would open his lips in a little gasp for
air, perfectly silent, yet expressive of a discomfort
which the older man had ceased to feel or else ignored.

John laid out his reed pens, fresh-sharpened, scruti-
nizing the point of each. The boy brought over the
ink, gliding carefully behind his master so as not to
touch him. For John was an initiated brother and must
not be polluted. John's long arm, which was reaching

out toward the scroll, halted halfway, motionless.

"My son," said John, "who was the girl with whom you were talking on the hillside?"

A vivid flush came up over the olive cheeks of the boy and spread into his forehead. He cast down dark eyes before his master and mumbled, "It is Deborah, daughter of Brother Joachim; and she lives in the great upper cave with Naomi, her mother."

"Where your duties do not lead you," said John dryly. "Those of us who marry are older men, long initiate, and prudent. Nor do they marry where they please, but make careful trial of the disposition of a woman for three years before concluding she is worthy to raise up sons to the House of the Pious. What business, therefore, have you to dally on the hill with Joachim's daughter?"

The boy started. "I had no such thought in my head. But Naomi lies sick and their waterpot is broken. Her daughter gave me a coin to buy another from the potter, since it is not permissible for her to come down to the House of the Pious. Then as it happened, my eyes fell on the coin, and I questioned her. Look at it, master!"

He put down the coin in front of John, who looked at it without touching. The brethren, except for those charged with such things, did not handle money.

It was a small silver coin struck with the image and inscription of Nero Claudius Caesar, across which, deeply incised so as to deface the portrait, were carved two words in Hebrew: "Freedom of Israel."

"Freedom of Israel!" sighed the young man, his face flushed.

"My son," responded John, looking at him gravely, "what has this freedom to do with the House of the Pious?"

"But if the Lord has shown His strength, shall we not praise Him? Do we not all look day and night for the deliverance of Israel? Why, master, the great Antonia fortress which kept Jerusalem in awe is stormed by the faithful. The palace of Herod is burned to the ground and its strong towers in our possession. On the Lord's altar, the sacrifice for Caesar is not offered any more."

"All this the brethren know," replied John tranquilly. "We have known these many days, but we judged the news unsettling for younger ears."

The young man clenched and unclenched his fists. "It is the hand of the Lord . . ."

"We are the Pious, my son, who have kept ourselves so pure from the world that the Temple sacrifices, nay the very High Priest himself is unclean beside us. If the Lord will do a great work, shall He not begin it among us rather than in Jerusalem, that wicked city? Do we not wait day and night upon His pleasure?"

"But . . ."

"The gutters of Jerusalem run blood, while those who are warlike cut down those who seek peace with the Romans. Does it concern us? They who call themselves servants of the Lord defile His Temple with the bodies of the slain. It is far wiser to let the wicked pursue their own ways. We are out of the world."

"Yet no great things are done here," cried the young man explosively. "Can we sit by while God delivers Israel?"

"My son," said John, looking at him steadily, "how long have you been with the brothers?"

"Ten years, master."

"Even so. Since you were eight years old. How long since I chose you for instruction?"

"It will be two years, come the rains."

"And come the rains, you may put on the white garment and join the brothers at the sacred meal if you have fortitude to endure three years' probation."

"It . . . always was . . . my desire."

John nodded gravely. "That is honestly said. Come now, I will ask you one more thing. Why was it that I chose you out of the other lads to be my pupil?"

The ghost of a smile trembled on the young man's lips, and he looked sideways at his master out of great dark eyes as though uncertain what he dare answer. Emboldened, however, by John's expression, he said, "Simply — or so they say — because my name is John."

John smiled in answer. "We-ell, it was partly so. There is a story in connection with our name which I have had it in my mind to tell you. Many years ago, the man most skilled among us in the reading of dreams and signs was one called Simon, of whom it was said that he had prophesied the disaster overtaking Arche-laus, who succeeded the great Herod. But at the time

I myself was young, Simon was an old man who had come back to our house to die after spending many years in our village communes. This Simon, then, fore-told that one from among us should perform a great service for God, and that he should be called John.

"Now at the time of which I speak there were three Johns among the Pious: old John the baker, a very worthy brother; I, myself, then seventeen; and another John born in the same month as I, likewise an orphan whom the brethren had adopted. This John and I were sworn as brothers. Indeed, we had actually mingled our blood as boys sometimes will and had vowed that we would do all things together. But though we toiled alike in the smithy and the workshop, joined in clean-ing out the great cistern for the rains, and slept in one cave, though in fact we did all things in common, it was steadily determined in my mind that he would per-form the great service for God and not I. There was a flame within my brother.

"Together we put on the white robe and entered the years of probation, as you will do, my son. These are hard years, neither bound by the great oath nor free from it, servant of the brothers still, yet weighted with the burden of the privations which they bear. If my brother grew silent and wrestled with himself, why, so did I, too. I thought nothing of it, but that this was another stage of our life's journey together.

"He woke me very early one morning long before day, saying, 'Brother, you must release me from my vow. I am going out into the world.'

"What could I do but beg him to remain, reminding him how even Israel sins in the sight of the Lord and merits rather His anger than His salvation? He answered, 'I know the world is evil, and for that reason there is work to be done in it. God calls me.' And for all my begging and praying, he would say nothing else.

"Well, I released him from his vow to me, and he went away. I never saw him again, but I can tell you what became of him. Some years later, he came up from beyond Jordan, calling on the people to repent and wash themselves in Jordan water, as our brethren do in the bath by the little cistern. Many came and repented of their sins, so that the fame of him spread over the whole nation. People spoke of him, because of what he did, as John the Baptizer.

"Yet see how evil is the world and how futile is the work of them who toil in it. Herod Antipas took my brother John and cut his head off, quenching his bright flame in blood. And the world went on in its wicked way, despite the outcry which he had made, despite the crowds and the washing and the loud repentance of sins. It is not one whit better. Nay, it is worse. There is more bloodshed, more hatred, lying, blasphemy, and uncleanness than there was then.

"Thus I alone was left of these three Johns, for John the baker, a decent, unambitious brother, was already dead. Most of my lifetime has been given to these scrolls, containing in them wisdom far more precious than gold. It is not a great thing I have done, but surely better than my poor brother John, though he burned with holy fire. Now you are called John, too; and it may happen that the great service is left for you, who are also among us. I would have you think of it when you put on your white robe at the coming of the rains and think also of my poor brother, who sowed in the salt sand and could reap nothing. Let him remind you to plow your furrow in the Lord's field, where God gives harvest."

He turned away to put out his hand to the scroll which he was copying. Very gently he undid the straps of the skin that covered it, smoothing it with his fingers, lest it be worn imperceptibly by his handling. As for the young man, he betook himself to his own copying of something much less sacred, namely a manual of the brothers' public rules, of which many copies were wanted.

Nothing more was ever said between John and his namesake of this old prophecy, but much was thought by them both. It was soon the time of the rains when the water came tearing down the gaps in the hills into the basin which the brothers had made for it, whence an aqueduct led it to the vast storage tanks in the building. Everything rejoiced in the water. For the brothers, it was a time for a great washing of soiled garments. For their goats and sheep, the sparse grasses in the pockets of the desert grew green. Such cropland as the place afforded must be planted early, lest when the dryness set in, there be no harvest. But amid all the bustle of the season, hearts were uplifted by the great festivals of the brethren, when those who had come for the purpose put on the white robe, while those who had worn it at the daily rite for three years became initiates and bound themselves by the great oath. These were occasions for outpourings of the heart, when old men prophesied and young men dreamed strange dreams. In the mind of the young John and of the older, there was constantly the thought of the great service. It was merely that the younger was filled with burning impatience to do some deed himself, while John the elder awaited with longing the time when God's purpose should be fulfilled.

It was still early in this season when the watchman upon the tower of the building saw that people were approaching from the north. Few travelers came this way; but some did pass, since Jericho was but a day's journey off, while to the south of them lay religious houses of smaller sects, and still further southward the rock fortress of Masada, built by the great Herod to overawe the countryside. Thus people passed up and down, and the House of the Pious gave hospitality to all, as was necessary in that desert region.

It was not, however, to watch for harmless pilgrims that a man was always stationed on the tower. The House of the Pious was well known to be rich, since each brother endowed it with the whole of his worldly wealth at the time of his entry. Desert raids were few, to be sure, since the coming of the Romans to Masada. Yet the land was never quiet. The House of the Pious itself was built like a fortress, while in the tower there was an armory plentifully furnished. The brethren were peaceful and all unpractised in arms, but they were ready to defend themselves if any should attack them.

The travelers now approaching were not desert people, yet they did not come peacefully either. There were, for one thing, about a hundred of them. For another, each was armed, some merely with reaping hooks or knives lashed onto stakes, but others with spears and swords and shields of real leather. They marched on foot, having with them two or three pack animals and driving before them a few goats, evidently spoils, quite possibly stolen from the flock of the brothers themselves, which was grazing in the open.

At the first sight of this unusual force, people had been sent running to call the brethren in, while women and children and those who chanced to be nearer to them took shelter in the caves. Yet though the oncoming mob could see this scurrying, it made no effort to pursue, merely breaking into discordant cries of triumph in which the Holy One was addressed as Lord and Savior of Israel. Somewhat emboldened by such zeal, the elders made no display of arms, but stationed themselves in the entry of the gate to force a parley.

The strangers came to a halt a few paces off, while he who seemed their leader put up his hand for silence.

"In the name of the King of the kings of the kings, the Lord of Israel," said he.

He was a middle-sized man, exceptionally burly, so much so that his mighty shoulders made him look shorter than he was. Vast brawny arms revealed his trade, which must surely have been that of a blacksmith. He was armed with a Roman sword and three knives in his waistband, while he wore on his massive head a Roman helmet.

"Praised be His name," agreed the presiding brother. "And may your coming be blessed. Tell us, though, your name and business."

"I am Simon, the captain of the Lord, called by men bar-Giora, the proselyte's son. I go against the fortress of Masada!"

The presiding brother, unused to strange emergencies, was bereft of speech. He knew the grim, almost impregnable fortress, and he knew also the power of the Roman soldiers against rabble. Though he said nothing, his silence was eloquent.

"The Lord has arisen, mighty in battle," cried Simon, raising his voice till it rang through the House of the Pious. "He has smitten the infidel in the pass of Bethhoron!"

Confused shouts broke from his followers at this, while what almost amounted to a hubbub arose among the brothers. It was known that the Roman, Cestius Gallus, with the army of Syria at his back was marching southward to reduce Jerusalem before revolt should spread through the entire country. The brethren had assumed he would take the city, though not out of any fear of the Roman might. They, too, trusted in the Lord, but it had not occurred to them that He would rise on behalf of the unclean.

"Who brought you this great news?" The presiding brother hardly knew whether to believe or not. Unquestionably, the ways of God were strange.

"Why, I, myself, was at Beth-horon," cried Simon bar-Giora unanswerably. "I took these spoils from the slain. Even as the angel of the Lord turned back Sennacherib, so he has put to flight Cestius Gallus."

"Great is the name of the Lord," admitted the presiding brother weakly. Even to his unworldly old age it was evident that if Gallus was really in flight, the countryside would be up. There was no other Roman army near them.

"He who is not with me is my enemy," shouted Simon bar-Giora. "Who comes with me to do God's work at Masada?"

"We are the Pious," replied the brother in haste. "We live apart and take no share in such things."

Simon bar-Giora put a hand on his sword. "I tell you, these are the days of the wrath of the Lord; and Israel is the instrument of His vengeance. Those who will take no share in this shall perish with the heathen."

Among the weaknesses of the presiding brother, cowardice held no place. The threats of Simon were backed up by his followers, who were bunching themselves as though for a rush. But the council of the Pious stood its ground.

"We are many more than you," the president said with dignity, "and we, too, are all armed. Nor is it against our rules to fight in our own defense. But if

you will save your strength to take Masada — when the
Lord will deliver it to you — then go with God. You
are too many to admit within our walls, seeing that
the brethren have long overflowed into caves on the
hillside. But if you will camp outside for the night, we
will send out people with water and such food as we
eat ourselves." Without the slightest haste, he turned
his back on Simon bar-Giora and retired within the
gate, which was without any loss of time barred behind him.

Simon bar-Giora's brow looked very black, but he
had some qualities of leadership other than blind
fanaticism. He fell to assuring his motley crowd that
the time of the Pious was not yet come. As for Masada
— they were but few as yet, but the Lord would raise
up numbers as the news of His glorious victory spread
through the country.

Thus cheered by hopes of future success, the men
camped willingly enough, though threats were muttered against those lordly ones who looked on at their
ease while others gave life and limb for the glory of the
Lord.

Presently the brethren, according to their word, sent
food and water. Since, however, the initiates might
not touch unclean men, all the bearers were servants
and novices, generally young men who were not bound
by the great oath. From this arose the brothers' first
misfortune. The miracle of a victory over the Romans
had jolted even the brothers out of their unworldly
thoughts. Small marvel, therefore, that those who

were not under oath and were of an age for action were carried away by desire to serve the Lord. Thus, in the morning when Simon's little army went on its way, its size was almost doubled. Those who departed were the younger men, on whom the brethren depended greatly.

Among those who left with Simon bar-Giora was the younger John, eagerly grasping his chance to do something great. It seemed to have come to him by special favor at the moment when he had put the white garment on, a sign of manhood. So the Lord went forth to war, and John followed after.

There were many wayfarers at the House of the Pious all that winter. It seemed the whole land was on the move. Simon bar-Giora, it was said, commanded ten thousand men; while the Roman garrison, lost in a sea of revolt, had abandoned Masada. Everywhere glorious things were reported. In the north, Galilee had risen for the Lord and was fortifying its cities. Further north still, the Romans gathered strength, awaiting spring. Nobody, however, spoke fearfully of the Romans now. What use for the Lord to manifest His power once if He would not do so again on behalf of His people?

Though matters went on in this way, the House of the Pious had fallen on evil times. All of these travelers robbed shamelessly, it being agreed among them that those about the Lord's work had a right to live off the produce of those who sat at home. On occasion, the brethren who guarded the flocks were actually murdered; while sheep and goats were snatched in increasing numbers. Worse still, the travelers made inroads on the food supply of the brothers, which could not be replenished, as had hitherto been their custom. No goods were to be had because no convoys were safe upon the road, except of the largest kind. The dislocation of so many farmers in the planting season was already a source of scarcity because the prudent foresaw a famine to come and started hoarding. Had it not been for the desertion of increasing numbers who were not bound by oath, the brothers themselves would soon have been facing famine. But the fewer they became, the harder it was to guard their own.

These troubles were discussed in the Assembly of the Many, which was the whole body of the initiate brothers. It was clear that some were for departing from custom and refusing hospitality to passers-by. Before this could be put into practice, however, the Romans invaded Galilee; and the Lord did not uphold His own. The people who came past the Pious now were either beaten soldiers, for whom to be caught meant crucifixion, straggling southward by devious ways, or else they were refugees. Women and children, whose houses were burned, whose menfolk were missing or dead, dragged themselves along with old people, cripples, or wounded limping beside them. Through the desert came but a mere trickle of these; but still many came and brought with them diseases, from which some score of the brethren died.

The news from Galilee grew worse and worse. In

Jerusalem, the richer sort, who were sophisticated people, well knew how futile it was to struggle with the
Romans. But as a peace party gained strength, so the
fanatics, swollen by refugees from the north, increased
mightily likewise. Soon in Jerusalem there raged a
a bitter struggle in which the zealots gained the upper
hand. Woe, then, to the well-to-do! Not only was
their loyalty suspect, but their wealth was needed to
carry on the war. There raged in Jerusalem a fearful
persecution in which vast numbers were killed, while
many others escaped out of the town with what they
could carry.

Suddenly the brethren, who had been hard put to it
with their depleted numbers, were swamped by fresh
recruits who came to them not for religion's sake,
but to get out of the war. It was hard to turn these
away, yet worse to discover that their own community now contained both robbers and murderers as
well as men of goodwill. The presiding brother, unequal to such troubles, took to his bed. Many like-
minded souls began to despair. Few brethren actually
deserted, because the curses invoked on those who
broke the oath were terrifying. There were, however,
groups of the Pious living informally, half in, half out
of the world, in several places. It began to be said that
in the Greek cities beyond Jordan, or in Babylon still
further east, men might find refuge.

After the failure of their head, the wiser brethren
turned gradually to the keeper of the scrolls, who was
strongest among them. John had little time these days

for the manuscripts which were his pride. His days were spent in dealing with all manner of crises, in spite of which the life of the house must go on. No matter what happened, every hour of the day and night the Scriptures were still studied. Indeed, the treasure of John's great library was actually enriched during these days, as one or two brothers whose minds the Lord had especially blessed poured out their prophecies, setting down the wisdom which had been revealed to them.

The conquest of Galilee took the Romans one whole summer, for there were many towns to be taken, and much slaughter was done. When at last the burned and devastated province was almost empty of men, the Roman army went into winter quarters and refitted for the invasion of Judaea in the spring.

That second winter, those who ruled Jerusalem had time to think of their inevitable doom. God had not saved Galilee. He had not vouchsafed His miserable people one small success to gladden their hearts. He had not spared them burning, massacre, disease, and famine. In Jerusalem, the rank and file still relied on God's holy Temple to protect them from the infidel. Those, however, who had risen to leadership were perforce realists. They had no thought of surrender, preferring death; but they squabbled for the glory of leading the people into the holocaust that God had prepared for them. Jerusalem now was torn apart by fanatics fighting against one another, some holding the Temple, others besieging them. Even the holy places were defiled with bloodshed, while the great granaries which would have provisioned a siege were burned to the ground.

Meanwhile, in the House of the Pious things went better. John had studied carefully each one of the brothers and selected a group of eleven, some young, some old, who could be relied on. Around these twelve, therefore, with John at their head, the brothers rallied. An effort was made to expel the unworthy. Organization gave better protection. Jericho, whose gardens had not yet been extensively plundered, was willing to sell a little food for a vast price. Yet as the rains settled in, John, too, must needs think of the future. "When the time comes," said he, among the chosen twelve as they met in the council chamber, "when the tide of war overwhelms us — as it will surely do unless God averts it — shall we desert the house or perish in its defence? We must decide."

There was a silence. It had always been the custom of the Pious to speak only in due order; and though John had relaxed the rule among themselves, old habits persisted.

"That is a hard decision," complained Matathias, who was in fact senior among them. "Need we make it thus early in the season? Is it not better to trust the Lord while we can? How may we encourage our brothers to work if secretly we are planning to break up the house?"

Judas, who was very nearly the youngest among them, shook his head with emphasis. "We must decide now. We are caught between two millstones and very likely cannot maintain ourselves for many weeks longer. To the south of us, Simon bar-Giora has eaten up the countryside and is extending his forces gradually in our direction. So far he has left the religious houses alone, but the treasure which we are known to possess would be useful to Simon in keeping his brigand forces together.

"Simon bar-Giora, they say, has no love for the Pious," agreed Andreas thoughtfully. "Did we not repulse him when he was only the leader of a rabble of half-armed husbandmen? He threatened us then."

"Whether or not he remembers this," said John with decision, "of one thing I am certain. Simon bar-Giora has proved himself no fool. When the Romans come south, do you think like Cestius Gallus they will march straight on Jerusalem? Or will they ravage the countryside first, so that when they come to the city, they may sit down at leisure to the siege of it, untroubled by risings in their rear?"

"They will ravage the countryside," said Judas. "It stands to reason."

"So I think myself," agreed John. "And so, no doubt, does Simon bar-Giora. What should he then do? He cannot meet the Romans in battle, but he can harry them and cut off forage parties. To do so, he must spread his tentacles far and wide, seizing on little outposts which can be defended for a while and which perhaps are not easy of approach for a large army. Such a place is the House of the Pious, convenient to him because it is near Jericho. And to Jericho the Romans will certainly come."

Another silence fell. If Simon bar-Giora were to be in their midst at any time, decision was indeed urgent. Simon's forces had an unenviable reputation.

"I for my part," said Matathias at last, "will die where I have lived. I am too lame to travel and would encumber the brethren."

"I am quite willing to die," Judas said, "but I will go. Those of the brethren who may reach a safe place will need leaders."

"That is wisely said," John agreed. "It is better that the younger men should go. I for my part will not desert our presiding brother, who is too ill to be moved."

Some said they would go and others that they would remain, but all joined in imploring John to lead those who should set out for a place of safety. His wisdom, which had sustained them so far, would be essential in keeping the brethren together. John shook his head. "I have a work to do here," he said. "I am chosen by the Lord to remain." No argument would move him.

In the end, more than half the brothers set out, though many were more afraid to go than to remain. In truth, the dangers seemed about equal. Those who left with Judas were going through a land where robbery, rapine, starvation, disease were commonplace, where all order had long ago broken down, where travelers were suspected of concealing money on them, or at the least something to eat. Even if they

came to the Greek cities, there was no telling that
they would find safety there. In Caesarea and the half-
Greek towns of Galilee, the faithful had risen against
the worshippers of idols and slaughtered them in heaps.
In retaliation, many Greek cities had massacred their
Jewish communities. Anywhere, a sudden spark might
set off a riot.

For these reasons, some stayed behind, more confident of God's protection in their house than they
were elsewhere. All the same, it was a gloomy group
that John faced on the following day when he took it
on himself to call the Assembly of the Many. The
House of the Pious was too big now. In the sixty-foot
refectory, long rows of empty benches emphasized the
numbers of those who had left. Enterprise and courage were at their lowest ebb. John, however, took no
notice.

"Brothers," he said, standing straight before them
in his long, white linen robe, as might Moses, lean and
tanned by the desert sun, have faced his people, "until
the Romans come or bar-Giora comes, we are still in
the hands of God. As long as His worship goes on
by day and night, there is life in our house. And while
there is life, there is work. We have a task to perform."

Eyes looked curiously at John, and the brothers sat
straighter. They needed someone to remind them that
God had a purpose for them, that they were not a useless remnant cast aside as rubbish.

"While there is yet time," John told them, "we must
preserve our treasure."

Looks changed to astonishment. The unworldly brothers had never thought much about their treasure, whose accumulation was only known to a few. It had been opened to supply those who went forth, but not too liberally, lest the word get abroad that these travelers were wealthy.

"What use to hide it?" asked Matathias wryly. "Simon bar-Giora has expert torturers to pry such secrets loose. Why should we care what happens to it? We do not need money."

"God forbid!" cried John with scorn. "Let him take our silver! Think, brothers, what is our true treasure? What indeed is the life of our house? Is it not the study of the Scriptures which goes on day and night? When this dies, we are all dead. When it revives again, wherever this may be, there lives the House of the Pious. What is our treasure, then — far more precious than gold? Is it not the fruits of our study, the knowledge we have gained of the Lord's ways? Is it not the scrolls in which all these things are written? Without them we should be poor indeed. This is the treasure that we must hide, so that when the House of the Pious is founded anew, as in God's time it will be, it may be rich through our efforts."

"That is indeed a great truth!" cried Matathias. "Brothers, shall we let the work of our lifetimes be lost? We will save our treasure!"

"Our treasure!" With a new alacrity the brothers set to work. There was much to be done, for the scrolls of the brethren numbered over a thousand. Each of them was packed in a jar and carried carefully to a hiding place in the caves.

"When they find our food stores and silver in the House," John said, "they will not care to search the country. But when our brothers come back, they will certainly visit the caves we have always used. They will find what we have laid up for them there, even if we have perished." He gave orders that the work should be carried on at night, lest travelers notice the coming and going.

The task was finished at last. The library was empty. John went over it himself lest a torn scrap remain; but there was nothing. "My life's work is ended," said he to himself, "and very possibly that service of which the prophet spoke has been done. For it is a great treasure which I have preserved." Sighing, he sat down in the vacant room and buried his head in his hands. It was as though his own life had been cleared out and was gone. He was dead now, and the house was dead. Without the Scriptures, the studies of the Pious went on no more.

As if at a signal, one of the brothers came rushing to find him. "Brother John, Brother John, come quickly! The watchman reports a mass of men to the southward."

"It is bar-Giora," said John with certainty. "He comes in God's good time." He drew himself up. "Go, open the armory. We will defend ourselves while we are able."

Simon bar-Giora had come up against the religious

houses in person, for the simple reason that he would
not trust their treasure to his lieutenants. Bar-Giora
was a wiser man in the ways of the world than he had
been, and he had no intention of allowing an independ-
ent command to be set up with the aid of the plunder.
He advanced, therefore, at the head of his men; and
he found his task unexpectedly easy. In no place was
resistance made except in the House of the Pious,
where the numbers of those defending were so small
that they merely served to irritate his army. Not that
the fate of the Pious was worse than that of the other
sects. In every case the army slaughtered, convinced
that the misfortunes of Israel were due to the lukewarmness of those who were not fighting.

In the train of Simon bar-Giora came the younger
John, still burning to do some great thing for the Lord.
He had not so far ever seen the enemy, that is the
Romans. Bar-Giora's fighting had been done at the expense of peaceful farmers. The more he harried and
burned, the more men joined him because, once destitute, they had nowhere else to go. Bar-Giora's brigands
had done terrible things, but they had done them in the
service of the Lord. The very unworldliness of John's
upbringing had helped him share this point of view.
Taught from childhood that the world was wicked, he
could accept the overturning of civilized life as sheer
necessity. His natural instincts were overcome, though
not without pain. It was truly hard for him to take his
part in the sack of the House of the Pious. He did so
as a sacrifice to the Lord in the hope of proving worthy.

John had already attracted bar-Giora's notice. There was a steely courage about him which won approval. He was quick to decide, and he had presence of mind. Bar-Giora had made John captain of a hundred, for he was wily enough to copy Roman organization without using the hated title of centurion. Secretly also he was eyeing John as a useful instrument. There are people who seem to have been made for the very purpose of being cast away in the forefront of the battle.

Bar-Giora had his men under control after his fashion. That is to say, none challenged his seizure of the silver, provided that the brethren's stores of food and wine and clothing might be plundered. Thus, instead of putting together supplies which might have lasted, they settled down to an orgy after their labors.

None of this was pleasing to John, whose personal habits were still abstemious. He accepted, perforce, the fact that even the champions of the Lord did evil, but he could not join in the celebration of victory over men whose lives had been blameless. He withdrew, therefore, and, seeking solitude, went up the watchtower, thinking he might commune with God and heal his soreness of spirit. But he did not find God there, for on the watchtower, dreaming his own dreams of power, stood Simon bar-Giora.

John would have withdrawn again, but Simon bar-Giora had noticed him and said, "Come here and tell me. You know this country, do you not? Here should lie Jericho. Those distant hills . . . they must be clear beyond Jordan."

"I know every foot of the place," agreed John. "For ten years it was my world." He looked about him. Below the cliffs, the sinking sun was making a dazzling path of gold across the sea, while behind them it shone full on the tumbled rocks through which the water came pouring after the rains. Though it was now the wet season, it so happened that the skies had been clear for some days and the beds were dry. In among them, however, the sun picked out small patches of green, contrasting with the lights and shadows of the rocks, sharp blacks and brilliant yellows, for the sun dyed everything with its own gold.

"There must be caves up there," said Simon, pointing. It was not easy to distinguish between shadow and true gap, but the yellow rocks did appear to be pocked with holes.

"Many caves," agreed John. "The brothers slept in them, for there were few dormitories in the house."

"Ah, easy of access, then."

"Not all. I and my fellows used to challenge one another to explore the higher ones which were not used."

Simon nodded his great head and seemed to ponder. "I think to leave you in command of this outpost, since you know the ground. You may send warning to Masada when the Romans come to Jericho."

The young man's face was radiant now with eagerness. The chance to fight the Romans instead of his own friends was a blessing bestowed on him by God. He said eagerly, "We will give a good account of ourselves to their scouting parties."

Simon studied him a moment, eyes a little narrowed. "Do not be too ready to fall back on the next house when they advance. War against Romans is not won by retreats, but by forcing them to expend two lives for one."

"Two lives for one! It is not enough," the young man cried. "Are we not warriors of the Lord? It shall be three!"

Simon nodded again as if to say, "I thought so!" His hand went up to his beard, and his dark eyes regarded the young man with a faint admixture of scorn. But John perceived nothing.

"A man foretold that I should do great service to the Lord," said he, taking to himself without a thought the words of the prophet. "Beside that, what does life matter?"

Simon's hand came down from his beard as though his mind was now made up. "There is indeed a great thing to be done. It might require someone who in God's service is above earthly temptation."

"I am the Lord's with my whole heart," John said. "There is no other thought in me."

"So I perceive." Simon's tone was dry. "You know of hiding places which would for a certainty be safe from the Romans?"

"I know of several."

Simon took him by the arm. "Come over here and stand by me, looking out at Jericho. If anyone comes up, you and I are talking merely of which way the Romans will come and how to avoid them." He low-

ered his voice. "I have had messages from those who
rule Jerusalem. They are thinking that before the town
is invested, it may be wiser to . . . scatter the treasures of the Temple."

The young man drew in his breath with a gasp. No
shrine in the world was as rich as the Lord's Temple.
To no other place on earth did tribute flow never-end-
ingly from all over the Empire and Parthia as well. The
heathen had many temples, the Jews but one. Besides,
the duty of giving was enjoined by the Law.

"If the Lord defend His Temple," Simon said, looking at him sideways, "the gold may be returned. If
not . . ."

"Why, then the gold may build another Temple!"
cried the young man, eager to shake off the impression
that the leaders in Jerusalem despaired of the war.

"So it may," agreed Simon, whose private use for it
was rather to sustain armies.

"No matter how vast it may be, I can hide it all!"

Simon shook his head. "It must be smuggled out in
small quantities for secrecy's sake and hidden in different places. You shall make me a record of where
each cache is placed and shall hide that."

"I will do it indeed," the young man answered, be-
wildered. "But is it not better that you should make
the list yourself, since all consignments will pass
through your hands."

"You have the hiding place," Simon said. "Besides,
I cannot write."

"Then I will do it as my service to the Lord," said

John. In his unworldly spirit, there was no thought of double-dealing — for which reason he never questioned why Simon should trust him. "The Temple treasure!" He was awed by the very thought.

"Remember, though," Simon said coolly, "three lives for one!"

Simon soon retreated with his plunder to Masada, leaving John in command at the House of the Pious while it wanted yet three months till spring. During those months many secret messages came to John, each one delivered by a different messenger. Simon had his methods of disposing of those who had once done this service. "In the cavity of the old House of Tribute," wrote John, "in the Platform of the Chain, sixty-five bars of gold." "In the stubble field of the Shaveh, facing southwest, in an underground passage looking north, buried at twenty-four cubits, sixty-seven talents." He was engraving the vast list on a copper scroll, supposing that it would prove more permanent than parchment. Sometimes his hand slipped in his haste, but he made the record as fair and detailed as he could, pausing sometimes to think of the fabulous resources of the Lord.

Time passed and the total swelled. The treasure of the Temple now in hiding had reached a ton of silver and very nearly half that weight in gold. Still more came in. But spring was coming too; and with the first greening of forage in the fields, the Romans marched.

They came on fast, their movements heralded by refugees ahead. As John sat over his scroll one early

March evening, the watchman on the tower saw a pillar of dark smoke rising over Jericho.

Now it was time for action! John sent a messenger racing southward with the news. He took himself out quietly onto the hillside, climbing in the moonlight past many a familiar cave in which lay, had he known it, the treasure of the Pious. His own treasure must be harder to find, for it contained secrets which the world would think of greater interest. Surefooted, he scrambled quietly amid the shadows into the shelter of his chosen cave.

Next morning he gave his men the watchword, "Three for one!" Down in Masada, Simon, smiling a little, shrugged his massive shoulders over John. Poor simple fool! The secret of the copper scroll was to be Simon's. It was better that the scruples of him who made it need not be consulted. Those in Jerusalem would have to reckon with Simon now as fully their equal.

John set out to sell his life dearly, but he did not after all exact three for one. The Romans knew the House of the Pious already, and they had intelligence from men in Jericho who were eager to save themselves from death. The Roman army, well led and disciplined, would have thought shame to itself if it were not more than a match for these irregular levies. John fell in his first combat, and his men scattered. But dying, he was aware that he had done his service.

In this way three men; John the prophet, John the scholar, and John the warrior, each performed his duty for the Lord. Their fates were unequal. The name of the prophet was remembered, though chiefly on account of what another did. The names of the other two and their achievements seemed to have crumbled into dust. For the House of the Pious was not inhabited again, while the Temple treasure was discovered here and there and carried off by unknown, lucky men. Neither Simon bar-Giora nor the leaders of Jerusalem survived the war, and the Jewish Temple was never rebuilt. Yet after two thousand years, the work of these two other Johns was discovered, a testimony to what men had selflessly done in fearful days to preserve the traditions of the Lord.